WILLIAM SHAKESPEARE

Hamlet

Retold by Margaret Tarner

D1217395

✳ MACMILLAN

MACMILLAN READERS

INTERMEDIATE LEVEL

Founding Editor: John Milne

The Macmillan Readers provide a choice of enjoyable reading materials for learners of English. The series is published at six levels – Starter, Beginner, Elementary, Pre-intermediate, Intermediate and Upper.

Level Control
Information, structure and vocabulary are controlled to suit the students' ability at each level.

The number of words at each level:

Starter	about 300 basic words
Beginner	about 600 basic words
Elementary	about 1100 basic words
Pre-intermediate	about 1400 basic words
Intermediate	about 1600 basic words
Upper	about 2200 basic words

Vocabulary
Some difficult words and phrases in this book are important for understanding the story. Some of these words are explained in the story, some are shown in the pictures, and others are marked with a number like this: ...³. Words with a number are explained in the Glossary at the end of the book.

Answer Keys
Answer Keys for the *Points for Understanding* and *Exercises* sections can be found at www.macmillanenglish.com/readers

Contents

A Note About The Author

William Shakespeare was born in Stratford-upon-Avon, a town about eighty miles north-west of London, in 1564. His father, John Shakespeare, was a well-known businessman, but he was often in debt. So, although William went to the local school, there was not enough money for him to go to university.

When Shakespeare was only eighteen, he had an affair with an older woman called Ann Hathaway. She became pregnant and they married in 1582. They had three children, but for most of his married life, Shakespeare lived in London.

In the sixteenth century, London was the only city in England. Young men who could not settle in their home towns often went to London to begin a new life. In spite of his marriage, Shakespeare decided to do that too. It is likely that he got the idea from seeing some travelling actors perform in Stratford.

We know that by about 1590, Shakespeare was living in London and working for one of the theatrical companies there. They were called The Lord Chamberlain's Men. Shakespeare worked first as an actor and later as a playwright. Although he returned to Stratford from time to time, Shakespeare's work kept him away from his family until the last few years of his life.

There were about 200,000 people living in London at this time and there were only four or five theatres for them to visit. These theatres were very different from modern ones. They were usually round or eight-sided buildings, and they held about 3000 people. The audience stood around three sides of the stage and there was no roof over the central part of the theatre, so neither the audience nor the actors had protection from the weather. Rich people would pay more to sit down under cover.

At the back of the stage, there were two balconies – one for the musicians and one for the actors. A small room under the balcony was separated from the rest of the stage by a curtain. Actors walked onto the main stage through two doors at the back. They performed very close to the audience. Plays had to take place in daylight, so they began at two o'clock. Sometimes six different plays were performed by a company in one week, so there was a constant demand for new plays.

A clever playwright could make old plays into new ones by adding characters, writing new speeches and even changing the story. Shakespeare became very good at doing this. He worked very fast and knew just what the audience wanted. He knew how to frighten people, and make them laugh or cry, and his plays became very popular.

Londoners could be influenced[1] by the plays they watched, so Shakespeare had to be very careful when he wrote them. His manuscripts[2] were always checked by a court official to prevent any treason[3] being written against the Queen.

Shakespeare's name soon became very well-known. Some playwrights were jealous of his success. Some laughed at him because he had never been to university, but others respected him and became his friends.

Shakespeare was a better businessman than his father. By about 1613 he retired[4] and returned to Stratford where he had bought a house. He lived there with his family until his death in 1616.

All the theatres where Shakespeare worked, including the Globe where his most famous plays were performed, were destroyed long ago. But there is now a new Globe on the South Bank of the River Thames. There you can see Shakespeare's plays performed just as they were in his lifetime. It is an exciting experience.

A Note About This Play

Shakespeare's tragedy *Hamlet*, is one the most famous plays ever written. A tragedy is a play in which the most important characters die or end their lives unhappily. These people are often great kings or princes who, because of some fault in their character, may be partly responsible for their fate[5].

The play was written when Shakespeare was at the height of his powers as a playwright – in the autumn of 1599. It was a disturbing time for England. Queen Elizabeth I was an old woman who was likely to die in the next few years, and people felt uneasy[6] about the future. This feeling of political unease forms the background to *Hamlet*.

The story of *Hamlet* was already well-known by the time Shakespeare wrote his version. The playwright did what he was good at – using old material to write a new play, with new language and new ideas.

Hamlet is a play about revenge[7], a popular theme at the time. Its hero is Hamlet, the young Prince of Denmark. The ghost of Hamlet's father, the late King Hamlet of Denmark, appears to his son, to tell him the dreadful truth: King Hamlet had been killed by his own brother, Claudius, who then made himself king and married Queen Gertrude, Hamlet's mother.

The ghost tells Hamlet that it is his duty to kill his wicked uncle and Hamlet agrees. But the prince is a thoughtful student, not a soldier. Even when Hamlet is sure of his uncle's guilt, the thought of killing does not come easy to him.

Everything that happens in the play now depends on Hamlet himself. We learn what he is thinking through speeches called *soliloquies* in which he speaks his thoughts aloud to the audience. These soliloquies help us to understand that Hamlet is a very complex and unhappy young man, who makes plans, but does not act until he is forced to.

Another theme of the play, which helps to confuse Hamlet's mind, is his relationship with the young girl, Ophelia. Hamlet, disgusted by his mother's love for Claudius, rejects Ophelia's love. This rejection, along with the death of Ophelia's father Polonius, brings tragic results.

Hamlet contains some of Shakespeare's finest poetry and the language of the play has a unique[8] power and beauty. The play was so popular that two versions were printed during the playwright's lifetime, in 1603 and 1604–5.

In 1623, two of Shakespeare's actor friends edited all 37 of his plays and printed them in one book.

Shakespeare, like other playwrights of his time, wrote his plays in a kind of poetry called *blank verse*. It does not rhyme, but each line has several strong beats, usually five. Speeches in blank verse can be learnt easily and they sound like normal English too.

Here are some examples in Shakespeare's own words.

(1) **Hamlet**   If it assume my father's noble person.
               I'll speak to it, though hell itself should gape.
(2) **Ophelia**   He took me by the wrist and held my arm.

Two lines that rhyme – a *rhymed couplet* – were often used to show the end of a scene.

(1) **Hamlet**   ... the play's the thing,
               Wherein I'll catch the conscience of the King.
(2) **Claudius** My words fly up, my thoughts remain below,
               Words without thoughts, never to heaven go.

About a quarter of *Hamlet* is written in prose, not poetry.

For more information about William Shakespeare, including projects and webquests, visit the students' section of www. macmillanenglish.com/readers

This Version Of Hamlet

This Macmillan Reader includes some 'real' extracts of text from *Hamlet*. We hope that these texts will help the students to both understand, and enjoy Shakespeare in the original. The extracts follow immediately after their simplified form. They are shaded in grey and have a separate glossary. In the glossary, words that are old English (no longer used in today's English) appear in italics. See the example (from page 14) below:

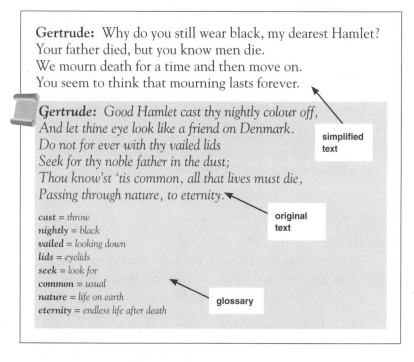

Gertrude: Why do you still wear black, my dearest Hamlet?
Your father died, but you know men die.
We mourn death for a time and then move on.
You seem to think that mourning lasts forever.

Gertrude: *Good Hamlet cast thy nightly colour off,*
And let thine eye look like a friend on Denmark.
Do not for ever with thy vailed lids
Seek for thy noble father in the dust;
Thou know'st 'tis common, all that lives must die,
Passing through nature, to eternity.

simplified text

original text

cast = *throw*
nightly = *black*
vailed = *looking down*
lids = *eyelids*
seek = look for
common = *usual*
nature = life on earth
eternity = *endless life after death*

glossary

The People In This Story

Hamlet

King Hamlet

King Claudius

Queen Gertrude

Polonius

Ophelia

Horatio

Laertes

9

Act 1, Scene 1

[The battlements⁹ of the King's castle, Elsinore, Denmark. It is night. A soldier, Francisco, is on guard duty¹⁰. Enter another soldier, Barnardo]

Francisco: Stop! Who's there? Stop and answer me!

Barnardo: Long live the King! I come to take your place, Francisco.

Francisco: I'm glad. It's very cold. All has been quiet tonight. The ghost has not appeared.

[Exit Francisco. Enter Marcellus and Horatio]

Barnardo: Welcome, good Marcellus. And Horatio too.

Marcellus: Horatio does not believe what we have seen, Barnardo.

Horatio: That's true. I've never seen a ghost and never will.

Barnardo: We've seen it twice. The ghost of our dead king was walking here.

At just this time, last night...

[Enter Ghost]

Marcellus: Look! It is here again! It is the King.

Speak to it, Horatio!

Horatio: What are you? Why do you walk at night?

You have the shape of the dead King of Denmark.

Speak to me now and tell me who you are!

[The Ghost walks on]

Barnardo: It is angry and it walks away!

Horatio: Speak! Speak! You must tell us what you are!

[Exit Ghost]

Marcellus: It has gone and will not answer.

Barnardo: So now, Horatio. Do you believe your eyes or not?

Horatio: It is the ghost of our dead king – King Hamlet.

He's wearing armour¹¹, as he did in battle,

When he killed old King Fortinbras of Norway.

Fortinbras and Hamlet had agreed to fight,
Over a piece of land that both states[12] wanted.
So Denmark won the land from Norway's king,
Land which young Fortinbras now demands from us,
Thinking our state is weak.
So now our enemies prepare for war and so do we.
Such war-like ghosts appear in time of trouble.
Is this is a warning to the state of Denmark?
[Enter Ghost]
Look where it comes again!
If you can speak, then tell me why you're here.
Oh, do not go again! Stay here and speak!
[A cock[13] crows. The soldiers try to stop the Ghost, but it walks away]
Barnardo: It was about to speak, but then the cock crew.
Marcellus: The bird of dawn warned it that the night was over.
When daylight comes, all ghosts return to darkness.
Horatio: Yes, look, the sky is red with the first light of dawn.
We must tell Hamlet we have seen his father.
The ghost will speak to him, I'm sure of that.

Horatio: *But look, the morn in russet mantle clad,*
Walks o'er the dew of yon high eastern hill;
Break we our watch up, and by my advice
Let us impart what we have seen tonight
Unto young Hamlet. For upon my life,
This spirit dumb to us will speak to him.

russet = *red-brown*
mantle = *cloak*
dew = *water seen on the ground in the early morning*
watch = *guard duty*
impart = *tell*

Marcellus: Let's do it. It's our duty.

11

Act 1, Scene 2

*[The Great Hall of the castle. Enter King Claudius, Queen
Gertrude, Hamlet, Polonious, Laertes and all the courtiers[14].
The King and Queen sit on their thrones and Hamlet, who is
dressed in black, sits by himself]*

Claudius: My brother's death brought sorrow[15] to our lives.

All Denmark mourned[16] him as a gracious[17] king.

But after sadness, joy has come again.

I am your king – Queen Gertrude is my wife.

My brother's queen is now my queen and Denmark's.

The state is stronger too and all men fear it.

[To Laertes]

I hear you wish to leave us – is that true?

Laertes: It is, my lord.

I came to Denmark for your coronation[18].

Now, with your permission, I'll return to France.

Claudius: Your father, Lord Polonius, is my dearest friend.

If he agrees, then so do I.

Polonius: I do, my lord.

Claudius: You are a good son, Laertes. You are free to go.

[He speaks to Hamlet]

My nephew, Hamlet, we are closer now.

Your mother is my wife – you are my son.

Hamlet: *[Very quietly]*

Closer by marriage – not in any other way.

Gertrude: Why do you still wear black, my dearest Hamlet?

Your father died, but you know men die.

We mourn death for a time and then move on.

You seem to think that mourning lasts forever.

Closer by marriage – not in any other way.

Gertrude: Good Hamlet cast thy nightly colour off,
And let thine eye look like a friend on Denmark.
Do not for ever with thy vailed lids
Seek for thy noble father in the dust;
Thou know'st 'tis common, all that lives must die,
Passing through nature to eternity.

cast = throw
nightly = black
vailed = looking down
lids = eyelids
seek = look for
common = usual
nature = life on earth
eternity = endless life after death

Hamlet: Seems? I know it does.
If I wear black or not, my grief[19] will never end.
Claudius: But life goes on, in spite of death, my son.
I am your father now – do not forget it.
And when at last I die, you will become a king.
Do not leave Denmark as you plan to do.
I need you here – so does your mother too.
Gertrude: Stay here with us, my dearest Hamlet.
Hamlet: I shall obey you, mother.
Claudius: That is a loving answer, my dear son.
Enjoy your life in Denmark. All men must honour[20] you.
[Exit everyone except Hamlet, who tells us his thoughts]
Hamlet: Enjoy my life? No, it is a great weight to me.
I do not wish to live in this sad world at all.
And Denmark is my prison. How I wish
That I could kill myself, but God forbids[21] it.
Everything that once seemed fair, disgusts me.
My mother's tears were false. Women cannot be trusted.

14

How could she marry her dead husband's brother?
How could her tears be dried so soon and turn to smiles?
In two short months, the tearful widow[22] has become
a whore[23].
No good at all will come from this quick marriage.
I know that's true, but yet I must say nothing.
[Enter Horatio and the soldiers]
Hamlet: My dear friend, Horatio! Welcome to Denmark.
Why are you not in Wittenberg?
Horatio: My lord. I came here for your father's funeral[24].
Hamlet: I think you came to see my mother's wedding!
Horatio: Indeed, that followed quickly.
Hamlet: My poor dead father! I can see his face!
Horatio: See? Where, my lord?
Hamlet: I see him in my mind, Horatio.
Horatio: I think I saw him yesterday, my lord.
Hamlet: Saw? The King, my father?
What do you mean, Horatio?
Horatio: For two nights past, the ghost of your dead father
has appeared.
These soldiers saw him – last night I saw him too.
We were on guard together and his ghost walked by us,
Dressed in his armour, but he did not speak.
Hamlet: How did he look? Was his face sad or angry?
Horatio: His face was pale and sad, my lord.
Hamlet: I must speak to him, Horatio.
I'll watch with you tonight.
My father's ghost! Something is wrong, I knew it.
He has bad news for me and I will hear it!
[Exit]

Act 1, Scene 3

[Enter Laertes and Ophelia]

Laertes: My dearest sister, I must leave you now.
My ship is ready, but before I go
I'll warn you once again about Prince Hamlet.

Ophelia: Why warn me? His words are full of love.
He sends me gifts and letters.
Prince Hamlet loves me, brother.

Laertes: Great princes are not free to love like other men.
They cannot choose their wives – they are chosen for them.
A royal marriage is decided by the state, not love.
Hamlet may say he loves you, don't believe it.
He gives you gifts and he wants one from you.
You, sister, have one precious gift – your chastity[25].
Hamlet may want it, but you must not give it.
Do you understand me, dearest sister?

Ophelia: Be sure I do. Your words are locked within
my heart.

[Enter Polonius]

Polonius: Now, Laertes, you must be on your way.
Take my blessing[26] with you.
Keep your money safe. Be honest, careful, true to all your
friends. Goodbye.

Laertes: I shall obey you father. Remember my advice, my
dearest sister.

[Exit Laertes]

Polonius: What advice? What did your brother say
to you, Ophelia?

Ophelia: Something about Prince Hamlet, father.

Polonius: I want to speak to you about Prince Hamlet.
You have been seen together many times.

You are having a relationship, I'm sure of that.
What has Prince Hamlet said? Tell me the truth.
Ophelia: With gifts and words he's told me of his love.
He has promised to be true and I believe him.
Polonius: You're thinking like a child, Ophelia!
When young men speak of love, do not believe them.
A young man's promises cover his desires.
Then words may lead to actions you'll regret.
You must not be alone with Hamlet any more.
Do you understand me, daughter?
Ophelia: Yes. I shall obey you, father.
[Exit Polonius and Ophelia]

Act 1, Scene 4

[The castle battlements. It is night. Enter Hamlet, Horatio and Marcellus]

Hamlet: It's very cold. Midnight has come and gone.
Will the ghost come tonight, Horatio?

Horatio: This is its usual time.

[Music is heard and the sound of great guns]
What does that mean, my lord?

Hamlet: My uncle, our King Claudius, is in a cheerful mood tonight.
There is a feast and every time he drinks, the music sounds.
The whole court cheers and then the great guns roar.

Horatio: Is that a custom[27]?

Hamlet: Yes, but not one my father followed.
Our enemies now think we Danes are drunkards
And not the fine soldiers that you know we are.
So one fault can ruin reputation[28] and make wise men look like fools.

[Enter Ghost]

Horatio: Look, my lord, it comes!

Hamlet: May all the powers of heaven help us. It is my father.
King Hamlet, royal Dane!
Why have you risen from your grave to find me?
No word was missing from your funeral speeches
And everything the Church wished for was done.
Why then have you burst out of your royal tomb[29]
Where you were laid to rest? And why do you return,
Dressed as a soldier, to terrify the living?
Speak, tell me what you want. Why are you here?
I fear you, dreadful ghost, but I must learn the truth!

May all the powers of heaven help us. It is my father.

[The Ghost beckons[30] to Hamlet and walks away]

Hamlet: The ghost wants to speak to me alone. Go on, I'll follow you!

Horatio: Do not go with it, my good lord. It may wish to harm you.

Hamlet: Why should I care? My life is worthless now. It cannot harm my soul. I'll follow it.

Horatio: It may take you into danger, my good lord. Or take another shape and drive you mad.

Hamlet: It has a message for me and I'll hear it.

Marcellus: I will not let you go!

Hamlet: You cannot stop me now! I'll kill you if you try! *[Hamlet follows the Ghost to another part of the battlements]* Speak to me here. I'll go no further.

Ghost: I am your father's most unhappy ghost, Who cannot rest until I have revenge!

Hamlet: Revenge? What must I do?

Ghost: Revenge my terrible and most unnatural murder!

Hamlet: Murder?

Ghost: Yes, murder.

Hamlet: Tell me what happened. My revenge will follow quickly.

Ghost: People were told a snake attacked me while I slept, And that its poison killed me, but the truth is worse. The wicked snake that killed me was my brother. He poisoned me and now he wears my crown!

Hamlet: My uncle! Oh, my God, I partly guessed it.

Ghost: My brother is a traitor[31] and a liar. He tricked[32] the people And he deceived[33] my wife. He married her, to cover his great sin[34]. How weak she was to listen to his lies.

To listen and believe them! It is too cruel.
But dawn is coming, I have more to tell.
As I slept beneath a tree, one afternoon,
My brother poured strong poison in my ear.
The poison acted fast – I did not wake
And so I died, with no time left to pray.
Hamlet: That was most cruel. Now I must kill the King.
Ghost: You must, but do not harm your mother, Hamlet.
Her conscience[35] will accuse[36] her foolish heart.
Now I must go, dear son. Remember me! Goodbye.
[Exit Ghost]
Hamlet: Remember you? Yes, I'll remember you.
All other memories will fade, but not your story.
Your foolish, wicked wife and her new husband,
The greatest villain[37] in the whole of Denmark!
Their names are written in the note-book of my mind.
I have sworn[38] revenge. Poor ghost, I'll not forget you!
[Enter Horatio and Marcellus]
Horatio: What news my noble[39] lord? What did it tell you?
Hamlet: Wonderful news!
Marcellus: Then tell us, my dear lord!
Hamlet: No, it's a secret.
Horatio: We will keep it safe, believe me.
Hamlet: Well then, all the wicked men we know,
are villains.
Horatio: We don't need a ghost to tell us that.
Hamlet: Yes, you are right, of course. I'll leave you now.
Thanks to you all, goodbye.
Horatio: Do you not trust us? We will keep your secret.
Hamlet: I'm sorry. Let me tell you, I believe the ghost.
It is an honest one. Now, one thing more,
Swear never to reveal[40] what you have seen tonight.

Ghost's voice: Swear!

Marcellus: We swear.

Horatio: I will obey the ghost. How strange this is! I do not understand it.

Hamlet: There are many things you do not understand, Horatio.

In days to come, you may not understand me either.

I may act strangely and seem a little mad. You must say nothing.

Swear that too before we go!

Ghost's voice: Swear!

[They swear]

Hamlet: You can rest now, unhappy ghost. Now, friends,

Remember what we all have sworn tonight.

These troubled times concern us all, Horatio.

But I'm the one man who can put them right.

Act 2, Scene 1

[Enter Ophelia, who meets her father, Polonius]
Ophelia: Oh, Father, Father, I am so afraid!
Polonius: Why, Daughter, what's the matter?
Ophelia: Just now, Prince Hamlet came into my room,
Carelessly dressed in clothes not even clean.
He was shaking and his face was pale.
His eyes were sad – oh, how he looked at me!
I fear the prince is mad.
Polonius: Mad for your love?
Ophelia: My lord, I do not know. But that is what I fear.
Polonius: What did he say?
Ophelia: That was the strangest thing – he did not speak
But took my arm and held it tightly.
And so he stood there, looking at my face.
Then he sighed twice and shook his head so sadly
That tears came to my eyes. And then he left me.
But as he walked, he did not turn his head.
To the last minute, he kept his eyes on me.
Polonius: The King must hear of this. His son's in love.
Love has sent Hamlet mad and that's a problem.
For love's a feeling that changes every man
And makes him do strange things.

Polonius: *This is the very ecstasy of love,*
Whose violent property fordoes itself,
And leads the will to desperate undertakings,
As oft as any passion under Heaven,
That does afflict our natures.

That was the strangest thing – he did not speak
But took my arm and held it tightly.

ecstasy = *madness*
violent = *very strong and harmful*
property = *feeling*
fordoes = *destroys*
undertakings = *actions*
passion = *strong feeling*
oft = *often*
afflict = *harm*
natures = *characters*

This cannot be our secret – the King must know it.
The truth's unpleasant and will trouble him.
But hiding it will only bring more pain.
Come, Ophelia.
[Exit Polonius and Ophelia]

Act 2, Scene 2

[Enter King Claudius and Queen Gertrude, with two young men – Rosencrantz and Guildenstern]

Claudius: Welcome, dear Rosencrantz and Guildenstern
And thanks for coming here so quickly.
We sent for you to watch our son, dear Hamlet.
Something has changed him – perhaps his father's death.
You know Prince Hamlet well, he trusts you both.
So please try to find out why he is so sad.
Rosencrantz: We'll do our best to help you, my good lord.
Guildenstern: We are both here to serve you.
Gertrude: My thanks to you, dear friends.
Now, don't waste time.
Speak to my son – he trusts you as good friends.
Rosencrantz: We'll do our best to help you, madam.
Gertrude: You have our thanks.

[Exit Rosencrantz and Guildenstern. Enter Polonius from the other side]

Polonius: My noble lord, I bring you both good news.
I think I know the cause of your son's madness.
Gertrude: His father's death and our quick marriage,
Both helped to send him mad.
Polonius: He's mad, that's true, but for a different reason.
I have a daughter, who has given me these.

[He holds up some letters and begins to read aloud]

'To the heavenly, the most beautiful Ophelia…'

Gertrude: Did Hamlet write that?
Polonius: Good madam, listen.

[He reads from several letters]

'I do not have the words to tell you how much I love you.'
Then he wrote this:

'Oh, dearest Ophelia. I love you best, oh, believe it.'
And here's another:
'But do not, oh do not doubt my love, my dearest lady.'
Claudius: But what did fair[41] Ophelia think about
these letters?
Polonius: Well, she was delighted to receive such
loving words.
She's very young and wanted to believe them.
But I'm her father and I knew my duty.
She had to learn the truth and so I told her:
'Lord Hamlet is a prince. He's far above you.
Stay well away from him. Send back his gifts and letters.'
And so she did. Now Hamlet's mad with love,
You must believe it.
Claudius: *[To Gertrude]*
Do you think that's true?
Gertrude: I think it is possible.
Claudius: But how can we be sure? Tell me, Polonius.
Polonius: I have a plan. Lord Hamlet often walks here,
by himself.
I'll tell Ophelia to walk here too.
You and I, my lord will hide and listen
And you will see if I am right or not.
Gertrude: But look, our son is coming now.
Polonius: Then go, dear madam, leave the Prince to me.
I'll question him.
*[Exit Claudius and Gertrude. Enter Hamlet from the other side.
He is reading]*
How are you, my good lord?
Hamlet: I'm well, thank you.
Polonius: Do you know me, my good lord?
Hamlet: Yes, I know you. You are a fishmonger[42].

27

Polonius: No, no, my lord, not me.

Hamlet: Well, you sell something and I hope you're honest. Do you have a daughter?

Polonius: Yes, I do, my lord.

Hamlet: Look after her then. Don't let her out when the sun is shining. She may get into trouble.

Polonius: *[To himself]*

All he thinks about is my Ophelia! But is he mad or not? I'll speak to him again.

[To Hamlet]

What are you reading, my good lord?

Hamlet: Words, words, words.

Polonius: What do they say, my lord?

Hamlet: That old men walk slowly. They say stupid things. They'd love to be young again.

Polonius: *[To himself]*

Well all he says is true. Is Hamlet mad or not? I'll find my daughter. What will he say to her?

[To Hamlet]

Would you like to rest, my lord?

Hamlet: Rest in my grave, is that what you mean, old man? How happy I would be to end my life!

Polonius: *[Worried by Hamlet's answers]*

I'll say goodbye, my lord.

Hamlet: *[To himself]*

These stupid old men!

[Enter Rosencrantz and Guildenstern. Polonius whispers to them]

Polonius: You want to speak to Hamlet – there he is!

[Exit Polonius]

[Rosencrantz and Guildenstern speak together]

Dear lord Hamlet! How glad we are to see you!

Hamlet: Welcome, my dear old friends!

What brings you to this prison?
Rosencrantz: Prison?
Hamlet: Yes, Denmark is my prison. There's no escape
From dreadful thoughts and dreams while I am here.
Why have you come to Denmark?
Guildenstern: To see you, my good lord!
Hamlet: No, that's not true. You were both asked to come.
The King and Queen of Denmark sent for you.
Rosencrantz: [Laughing]
You are right, my lord. They did send for us.
Hamlet: And I know why. I have been so unhappy lately
That I have lost all interest in my life.
The beauties of the world mean nothing to me.
And man, the finest work of God's creation,
Is nothing more than dust. I see you smiling,
But women do not please me either.

Hamlet: *What a piece of work is a man! How noble in reason!
How infinite in faculty! In form and moving how express and
admirable! In action, how like an angel! In apprehension, how
like a god! The beauty of the world, the paragon of animals; and
yet to me, what is this quintessence of dust? Man delights not me;
no, nor woman neither.*

reason = ability to think
form = shape
express = impressive
apprehension = understanding
paragon = best example of
quintessence = a pure example

Guildenstern: No, my good lord.
That's not what we meant at all.
But we have news that we are sure will please you.

Hamlet: What news is that?

Rosencrantz: My lord, the players[43] have arrived. Would you like to see them?

Hamlet: Indeed I would. They are welcome here and you are too.

Welcome to Elsinore, friends, though you were sent for.

My uncle-father and aunt-mother think I'm mad.

But they are wrong.

I'm only mad sometimes – when the north wind is blowing.

Be sure you tell them that!

[Exit Rosencrantz and Guildenstern]

[Enter, from the other side, Polonius and the players]

Hamlet: Welcome good friends! I am glad to see you.

You all must act for us tomorrow night.

[To the First Player]

You've grown a beard since I last saw you!

And here's the boy who plays the woman's part.

You've grown taller, my young sir.

All of you are welcome to the court of Denmark.

[To Polonius]

Look after them. Give them a royal welcome.

These men are more than actors.

They portray kings and comment on their actions.

A player's words can change the way men think.

[To the First Player]

I'll speak to you alone. Wait here a minute.

[Exit Polonius with the other players]

Hamlet: Do you know the play 'The Murder of Gonzago'?

First Player: I do, my lord.

Hamlet: Good. Then act it before the King tomorrow night.

I'd like you to add a short speech that I'll write for you.

Could you do that for me?

First Player: I could, my lord.
Hamlet: Thanks. Then I'll see you later.
[Exit First Player]
Hamlet: These men are actors, that's the job they do.
Words are their work, they play many parts
And everyone agrees they are the best.
But what am I? What is the part that I'm playing?
Fool that I am, I have been wasting time
And have forgotten what I swore to do.
Many men would say that I'm a coward[44]
Who dares not kill the man who killed my father.
My uncle is a traitor and a wicked villain
And he deserves to die. Words will not kill him
But my dagger[45] will. So, no more words, but actions!
I've wasted too much time, but now my plan is clear.
These players must act out the murder of my father.
I'll watch my uncle. And when he sees the play,
His guilty mind will tell me all he knows!
The Ghost may be a devil[46] sent to trick me,
And take me down to hell. This play will prove
My uncle's guilt. Then I'll be sure
A wicked villain rules in Elsinore!

Act 3, Scene 1

[The next day. Enter King Claudius, Queen Gertrude, Polonius, Ophelia, Rosencrantz and Guildenstern]

Claudius: *[To Rosencrantz and Guildenstern]*
So Hamlet has been too clever for you.
That is the whole truth, isn't it, my friends?
Rosencrantz: He feels confused, my lord, or so he tells us.
Guildenstern: But even so, he hides his feelings from us.
Gertrude: He needs something new to interest him.
Is there nothing we can do?
Rosencrantz: I think there is. The players have come to court.
They will act here tonight.
Polonius: *[To Claudius and Gertrude]*
Yes, and Prince Hamlet wants you both to see the play.
Claudius: That is good news. Make sure he does not
change his mind.
Rosencrantz: We shall, my lord.
[Exit Rosencrantz and Guildenstern]
Claudius: Sweet Gertrude, leave us.
Hamlet is coming here and he will see the fair Ophelia.
When he speaks to her we'll learn the truth about his madness.
Polonius and I will hide ourselves and listen.
Gertrude: I hope your beauty is the reason for his madness.
Tell him you love him and all may yet be well.
Ophelia: Madam, I will.
[Exit Gertrude]
Polonius: Now, daughter, take this book of prayers
and read them.
Then my lord Hamlet will be sure you're honest.
This trick of mine will hide the truth, I'm sure.
Claudius: *[To himself]*
Oh, God that's true. How he has whipped[47] my conscience!

For I have covered up my wicked deed[48] with pleasant words
As an old whore will paint her face to make herself a beauty.
Polonius: [To Claudius]
Come, my good lord, let us hide and listen!
[They both hide behind a tapestry[49].]
[Enter Hamlet]
Hamlet: [To himself]
What must I do? Shall I decide to live or die?
Do I have strength enough to go on fighting –
To overcome the problems that I face?
If I kill my uncle, my own death will follow his.
Then why not kill myself and make an end?
If I died now, then I would sleep forever.
My troubles ended in the sleep of death.
But when we sleep, we dream.
How terrible those dreams of death might be!
The fear of what comes after death is greater
Than the fears of life we know.
So fear of life and death confuse my thinking.
I cannot yet decide what I should do.

Hamlet: *To die, to sleep,*
To sleep, perchance to dream; ay, there's the rub,
For in that sleep of death, what dreams may come,
When we have shuffled off this mortal coil.
Must give us pause.

perchance = *perhaps*
rub = *problem*
shuffled off = *got rid of*
mortal coil = *terrible trouble of our life on earth*
pause = *give us pause – make us stop to think*

[He sees Ophelia]
But here's the fair Ophelia. Pray for me sweet maid.

33

Ophelia: My dear lord Hamlet, I am glad to see you.
Here are the gifts you sent. I must give them back.
Hamlet: Gifts? No, I gave you nothing.
Ophelia: My good lord, you did.
And gave me loving words that I believed were true.
But now I see that all your love has gone.
Here, take back your gifts. They're worthless without love.
Hamlet: I wonder, is a woman ever honest?
I thought I loved you once, Ophelia.
Ophelia: I truly thought so too.
Hamlet: Then you were wrong. It was not love at all.
Go to a nunnery – a brothel, if you like.
Your beauty will not save you. You will be blamed
However honest that you say you are.
Young men like me are dangerous, you know.
We are not honest either – I'm the worst of them.
So here's my advice to you: Don't marry anyone.
But if you must, don't have a child.
There are enough sinners in the world already.
[Hamlet hears a noise]
Is someone listening to us? Where's your father?
Ophelia: He is at home, my lord.
Hamlet: If that's the truth, tell him to stay there, then.
Goodbye.
You are not honest, though you are so fair.
I know that now.
Don't try to make a fool of me again. Goodbye.
Ophelia: *[To herself]*
Oh God, I think he's mad. What can I do?
Hamlet: Women are all the same. How cleverly they
trick us!
They put on make-up and they dance about.

Is someone listening to us? Where's your father?

They laugh and smile to make themselves attractive,
Oh, how I hate them! They will drive me mad.
There must be no more marriages in Denmark.
Those who are married already – they are safe
Except for one. Go now, Ophelia.
Never think of love again, or of me, either.
[Exit Hamlet]
Ophelia: How strange his words are! I am sure he's mad!
And I am most unhappy.
Prince Hamlet was the bright star of our court.
The perfect courtier – scholar and soldier too.
All men looked up to him. Now he is mad.
His mind's confused and everything has changed.
By his sweet words. Now both our lives are ruined!
[Enter Claudius and Polonius]
Claudius: Love?
[He laughs]
No, love's not sent him mad.
I'm not sure that Hamlet's mad at all.
But something's troubling him and that troubles me.
This is my plan – I'll send him off to England
To get some money that is owed me there.
Away from Denmark, he will forget his madness.
What do you think of that, Polonius?
Polonius: It's a good plan, but I still think
That love for my fair daughter made him mad.
Now I have another plan, to make things sure.
Let the Queen, his mother, question Hamlet.
I'll hide myself and listen while they talk.
He may tell her what his true feelings are.
Claudius: Yes, I agree, for I must know the truth.
Madness in great men, must be watched.

Act 3, Scene 2

The Great Hall of the castle. [Enter Hamlet, who meets Horatio]
Hamlet: Welcome, Horatio, my dearest friend – my only friend, I mean,
For I can trust no other man in Denmark.
You are a man I know I can rely on.
Whatever happens, you are true and honest
And closest to my heart, my dear Horatio.
Horatio: I'm always at your service, my dear lord.
Hamlet: Tonight the players act before the King
And I want you to watch him closely.
You know the secret of my father's death, Horatio.
Horatio: I do, my lord.
Hamlet: Some words I've written should reveal
my uncle's guilt,
If they do not, the Ghost was sent from Hell to damn[50] me.
Horatio: I shall watch the King, my lord.
Hamlet: And I shall play the madman! Here they come!
[Enter Claudius, Gertrude, Polonius, Ophelia, Rosencrantz and Guildenstern and all the courtiers]
Claudius: How is my dear son, Hamlet?
Hamlet: Well, very well.
Gertrude: My dear Hamlet, come and sit with me.
Hamlet: No, Mother. Here's a pretty girl. I'd rather lie with her!
[Hamlet sits on the ground next to Ophelia and speaks to her]
It makes me so happy, sitting close to you.
Ophelia: That pleases me, my lord.
Hamlet: My father died only two hours ago
And look, my mother's smiling! So I'll smile too!
Ophelia: Your father died four months ago, my lord.

Hamlet: As long ago as that? And people still remember him? Then I must dress like a sad old man. I am too old for love.
Ophelia: Please be quiet, my lord! The play's beginning now.
[Enter two actors playing the King and the Queen]
King: For many years, we've lived together happily
But now my time is coming to its end.
I must say goodbye to you, my dearest wife
Before the coming day that ends my life.
Another husband you must take, my dear.
For you will be alone, when I'm not here.
Queen: A second husband never will be mine.
For that would kill the first a second time!
King: You say that now, but after I am dead
You'll let another husband share your bed.
Queen: No, no. I will be punished all my life
If once a widow, I become a wife!
King: I hope that's true. Now I will sleep here in my garden.
Queen: May sleep bring rest to you!
I promise you, I always shall be true!
[Hamlet, to Queen Gertrude]
Hamlet: Madam, what do you think of this play?
Gertrude: I think that the Queen protests too much.
Hamlet: Oh, but she'll keep her promises, I know she will.
[Claudius is looking very unhappy. He speaks to Hamlet]
Claudius: What is this play about?
I hope it won't cause trouble.
Hamlet: Trouble? No, it's all good fun. Their words will make you laugh.
Here comes the poisoner now.
Claudius: Poisoner? What do you mean? What's this play called?

Poisoner? What do you mean?

Hamlet: It's called 'The Mousetrap'. It's about a murder.

Look, here comes Lucianus the murderer!

He's the King's nephew. Listen carefully!

Lucianus: Now is my chance.

The King's asleep and no one's near.

I'll pour this deadly poison in his ear.

[Hamlet speaks to Claudius]

Hamlet: You see, the King is poisoned in the garden.

His nephew gets his crown and the Queen's love too!

[Claudius stands up. He looks very frightened]

Ophelia: The King has stood up.

Gertrude: You are ill, my dear lord. Let me help you.

Polonius: Stop the play!

Hamlet: Frightened by a play? What kind of king is that?

Claudius: Stop, stop! I've seen enough.

Lights! Light more torches.

Give me more light! I must get away.

All: Lights, lights!

[Exit everyone except Hamlet and Horatio]

Hamlet: Oh, good Horatio! I was right.

The Ghost told me the truth.

I'd bet[51] a thousand pounds on that.

Did you see what my uncle did?

Horatio: Yes, my lord.

Hamlet: The talk of poison frightened him at once.

My uncle's guilty conscience has damned him.

[Enter Rosencrantz and Guildenstern]

Guildenstern: My lord, we must speak with you.

Hamlet: Say anything you like and I shall listen.

Guildenstern: King Claudius is most upset, my lord.

Hamlet: What has upset him? Has he drunk too much wine?

Guildenstern: No, he's very angry.

He's almost mad with anger!

Hamlet: Mad? Like me? Send for a doctor then.

Guildenstern: This is a serious matter.
Your mother has sent me to you.
Hamlet: How kind of her. You are most welcome, sir.
Guildenstern: Your mother is upset by your behaviour.
Hamlet: The whole court knows I'm mad. I cannot help it.
Rosencrantz: The Queen thinks that you can.
She wants to speak to you at once.
Hamlet: Then, like a loving son, I'll go to see her.
Rosencrantz: My lord, I used to be your friend.
We want to help you.
Hamlet: No one in Denmark can help me now.
You are my uncle's spies[52], we cannot be friends.
I'll tell you nothing.
[Enter Polonius]
Polonius: My lord, The Queen must speak to you – at once.
Hamlet: She wants to see her mad son, does she?
Tell her I'm on my way.
Now leave me, all of you.
[Exit Rosencrantz, Guildenstern and Polonius]
Hamlet: *[To himself]*
The night has come, when men do wicked things.

Hamlet: *'Tis now the very witching time of night,*
When churchyards yawn and hell itself breathes out
Contagion to the world. Now could I drink hot blood,
And do such bitter business as the day
Would quake to look on.

witching = *wicked and frightening*
contagion = *disease*
bitter = *terrible*
quake = *shake with fear*

I could kill too, but I must not harm my mother.
She has done wrong and I must tell her so.
My words will wound[53] her, but I will not kill her.

Act 3, Scene 3

[Enter Claudius, Rosencrantz and Guildenstern]
Claudius: My dear son's madness has become very dangerous.
It is not safe to keep him here in Denmark.
I'm sending him to England. You'll go with him.
Guildenstern: Until then, we'll keep you safe, my lord.
Rosencrantz: When the King's not safe, the country suffers.
Claudius: That's very true. Get ready for your journey now.
While Hamlet's here, his madness grows.
So grows the danger too. I am not safe.
[Exit Rosencrantz and Guildenstern. Enter Polonius]
Polonius: Lord Hamlet's going to his mother's room.
I'll hide myself to hear what they will say.
Claudius: Thanks, my dear lord.
[Exit Polonius]
Claudius: *[To himself]*
I am a man who has murdered his own brother!
How can I say I'm sorry when I wear his crown?
How can I ask forgiveness when I have his queen?
My heart is black with sin, but I will try to pray.
[Claudius kneels down to pray. Hamlet sees him, as he walks by]
Hamlet: *[To himself]*
How easy it would be to kill him now!
Too easy. He is praying and would go to heaven.
My father had no time to pray before his death,
His brother was too cruel. I'll kill my uncle
When he's doing wrong and then he will be damned.
I must go to my mother.
[Exit Hamlet. Claudius stands up]
Claudius: I cannot pray. I say the words, but do not
mean them.
My heart's too black.

Act 3, Scene 4

[The Queen's room. Enter Gertrude and Polonius]

Polonius: Your son is coming. I will hide myself and listen. Tell him how angry and upset you are.

Gertrude: I will. Hide yourself quickly. I hear him coming.

[Polonius hides behind the tapestry]

Hamlet: *[Outside the room]*

Mother, mother, mother!

[Enter Hamlet]

Hamlet: Now, Mother, what's the matter?

Gertrude: Hamlet, you have made your father very angry. Why?

Hamlet: Mother, you have made my father very angry. Why?

Gertrude: That's a mad answer.

Hamlet: And your question was a wicked one.

Gertrude: Don't speak to me like that. Have you forgotten who I am?

Hamlet: You are the Queen – your husband's brother's wife And, although I wish you weren't, you are my mother. Sit down with me. You will not leave until you have heard the truth!

Gertrude: Hamlet, you're mad. Will you murder me? Help! Help! Fetch someone! Help!

Polonius: *[From behind the tapestry]*

Help! Help!

Hamlet: What's that? There's something there. A rat – I'll kill it.

[Hamlet takes out his sword[54] and pushes it through the tapestry. Polonius cries out]

Gertrude: Hamlet, what have you done?

Hamlet: I don't know. Is it the King?

Gertrude: What a wicked, wicked deed!

What's that? There's something there. A rat – I'll kill it.

Hamlet: A wicked deed? Almost as bad, good mother
As kill a king and marry his own brother.

Gertrude: As kill a king?

Hamlet: That's what I said.

[He pulls back the tapestry and sees Polonius]

Hamlet: Stupid old fool. I thought you were the King.
You've played your last trick on me. And so, goodbye.

[To Gertrude]

Now I will tell you what I've come to say. Sit down.

Gertrude: What have I done? Why do you speak to me
like that?

Hamlet: I'll tell you what you've done, although I'm
ashamed[55] to say it.
You've made a mockery[56] of your marriage vows[57] –
The ones made to my father. Then you were young,
But now, in middle age, you've given way to lust[58].
Your second marriage has made heaven blush.
Look, here's my dead father's portrait[59]. What a man he was!
Honest and kind – a soldier and a king.
And here's my uncle's portrait that you wear close
to your heart.
Can't you see the difference, are you blind?
And yet you took him for your second husband!
You cannot love him, it was shameful lust
That led you to his bed and wicked incest![60]

Gertrude: Oh, dearest Hamlet. Your words show me a mirror
of my sin
That's left such black marks in my soul, dear Hamlet.
They cannot be removed.

Hamlet: And yet you go on making love to him –
Night after night. It is a kind of madness.
Oh, wicked woman! Do you have no shame?

Gertrude: Enough, dear Hamlet! You must pity me.

Hamlet: You're married to a murderer, a liar,
A wicked man, who stole the crown of Denmark
And put it in his pocket like a common thief.[61]
Gertrude: No more!
Hamlet: A worthless and unworthy king…
[Enter Ghost. Hamlet can see him, but Gertrude cannot]
Hamlet: *[To Ghost]*
You come again. Oh, save me, Heaven!
You come to chide[62] your disobedient[63] son.
Gertrude: Oh, God, he's speaking to the air! He's mad.
Ghost: My son, have you forgotten what I told you?
Revenge, Hamlet, revenge! Revenge for murder.
Comfort your mother now. She will repent[64].
Speak to her, Hamlet.
Hamlet: *[To Gertrude]*
How are you, lady?
Gertrude: And how are you? You speak to empty air.
What are you looking at, my dearest son?
Hamlet: At my poor father's ghost. How pale he looks!
Gertrude: Your father's ghost? I can see nothing.
Hamlet: Look! There he goes. He's leaving now.
[Exit Ghost]
Gertrude: This is your madness, my dear son, believe me.
Hamlet: Mad? No, I'm not mad. Don't make that your excuse.
Admit your sins and then confess[65] to heaven.
Repent of what you've done and sin no more.

Hamlet: *Lay not a flattering unction to your soul,*
That not your trespass, but my madness speaks:
… Confess yourself to Heaven,
Repent what's past, avoid what is to come.

46

flattering = *making something better*
unction = *something put on a wound to heal it*
trespass = *sin, crime*
soul = *the part of a person that lives forever*
confess = *tell someone about the bad things you have done*
repent = *say one is sorry*
avoid = *keep away from*

My words are cruel, but they are meant to help you.
Gertrude: Oh, Hamlet. You have cut my heart in two.
Hamlet: Then throw away the bad part. Live with the good.
But you must make this promise.
Do not make love to Claudius again. Don't let him
touch you.
I am not mad, I just pretend to be.
He's sending me to England. Did you know?
Gertrude: I had forgotten that.
Hamlet: My two old friends go with me, but I do not
trust them
More than I would trust two poisonous snakes.
The King has made a plan. This old man was part of it.
But I can make plans too.
[Hamlet looks at the body of Polonius]
I'm sorry now I killed him, but I'll take the blame.
I'll get him out of here. Goodnight, dear mother.
This old man was far too stupid when he lived.
He spoke before he thought and was a liar.
But now he's grave and silent.
Silent as the grave itself.
[Hamlet laughs]
Goodnight, good mother.
[Exit Hamlet, dragging Polonius' body after him]

Act 4, Scene 1

[Enter Claudius. He speaks to Gertrude, who is crying]
Claudius: You must tell me what's the matter.
How is Hamlet?
Gertrude: He is mad for sure.
Mad as the angry sea. And cruel too.
He heard a noise and in his angry rage[66], took out his sword
And with it killed that good old man, Polonius.
Claudius: Oh God! If I'd been there, I would be dead
by now.
This death will still make trouble for me. I'll be blamed
Because I did not keep Prince Hamlet locked away.
Where is he now?
Gertrude: I don't know. He took the body somewhere.
He's sorry now, I'm sure.
Claudius: His ship must sail before the sun is up.
And I must plan how I can cover up this murder.
Ho, Guildenstern!
[Enter Rosencrantz and Guildenstern]
My mad son, Hamlet, has killed old Polonius
And taken him away. Look for Prince Hamlet,
try to calm him,
Then take the old man's body to the chapel[67].
Bad news travels quickly, this must be concealed[68].
If we are careful, blame will not fall on me.
Come with me, my dear Gertrude, come away.
My heart is full of terror and dismay[69].
[Exit Claudius and Gertrude]

Act 4, Scene 2

[Enter Hamlet, without the body]
Hamlet: That's safely hidden!
Rosencrantz and Guildenstern: *[Shouting off-stage]*
Hamlet! Lord Hamlet!
Hamlet: Who's that calling my name?
[Enter Rosencrantz and Guildenstern]
Rosencrantz: What have you done with the dead body, my good lord?
Hamlet: My good lord? He's where you'll find him.
Rosencrantz: You must tell us where he is.
Hamlet: He's with the King – the dead king, not the living one.
Guildenstern: King Claudius wants to see you. We have come to take you to him.
Hamlet: Then you must catch me first!
[Exit Hamlet, running. Rosencrantz and Guildenstern follow him]

Act 4, Scene 3

[Enter Claudius, from the other side of the stage]
Claudius: *[To himself]*
We must find the body and Prince Hamlet too.
While he is free, he is a danger to me.
The people love him and, if he is harmed,
They will blame me, not him.

Claudius: *I have sent to seek him, and to find the body:*
How dangerous is it that this man goes loose:
Yet must not we put the strong Law on him:
He's loved of the distracted multitude,
Who like not in their judgement, but their eyes.

goes loose = *stays free*
distracted = *stupid, unthinking*
multitude = *people [of Denmark]*
like = *decide [without thinking]*

Yes, he must go to England straight away.
I'll say I planned the journey long ago.
[Enter Rosencrantz]
What's happened? Have you got the body?
Where's Prince Hamlet?
Rosencrantz: We have the prince, my lord. He is
well-guarded.
Claudius: Then bring him here.
Rosencrantz: Ho, Guildenstern, bring in the prince.
[Enter Hamlet, Guildenstern and some guards]
Claudius: Tell me, Hamlet. Where's Polonius?

Hamlet: Well, he's at supper – not where he eats, but where
he's eaten.
Maggots[70] and worms will make a meal of him!
Claudius: Tell me at once. Where is Polonius?
Hamlet: He may have gone to heaven or to hell.
You can send anyone to look for him in heaven.
Or go to hell and look for him yourself.
But very soon, you'll smell his body on the lower stairs.
Claudius: *[To guards]*
Look for him there.
[Exit guards]
[To Hamlet]
You are not safe here – you must leave at once.
For England!
Hamlet: England?
Claudius: Yes, for England.
Hamlet: Then, goodbye, dearest mother.
Claudius: I am your loving father, Hamlet.
Hamlet: Father, mother, it is all the same.
But I must leave for England!
Claudius: *[To Rosencrantz and Guildenstern]*
Follow him. Get him on the ship at once.
You must all leave tonight.
[Exit Rosencrantz and Guildenstern]
The English king bows to my Danish power.
My letters order him to kill the prince.
Obey me, English king! While Prince Hamlet lives,
I'm like a sick man with a deadly fever.
And when he dies, I'm cured. But now I live in dread[71]
And shall not be at peace 'til Hamlet's dead.
[Exit Claudius]

Act 4, Scene 4

[Enter Fortinbras, with his army]

Fortinbras: Go Captain, greet the Danish king from me.
Tell him that Prince Fortinbras of Norway seeks[72] permission
To march[73] across his land. I ask him as a friend.

Captain: I will, my lord.

Fortinbras: Then I shall go on.

[Exit Fortinbras and his army. Enter Hamlet, Rosencrantz and
Guildenstern. They are on their way to the ship for England]

Hamlet: [To the Captain]
Good sir, whose soldiers are these?

Captain: They are from Norway, sir.

Hamlet: Then what are they doing here?

Captain: They are marching towards Poland, sir.

Hamlet: Who is in charge and why are they going there?

Captain: Young Fortinbras, nephew to the old king of
Norway, is leading them. He wants to take back a small piece
of land his father lost. It's worthless though.

Hamlet: Then the Poles will give it back. There'll be
no fighting.

Captain: No, you are wrong, sir. The Poles plan to defend it.
They'll fight until their last soldier's dead. I must go.
Goodbye, sir.

[Exit Captain]

Rosencrantz: [To Hamlet]
We must go on too, my lord.

Hamlet: Leave me here alone. I'll be with you in a minute.

[Exit Rosencrantz and Guildenstern]

How true it is, that everything I see
Reminds me my revenge has been forgotten.
A man is better than an animal
For he has reason. He can think and plan.

Hamlet: *How all occasions do inform against me,*
And spur my dull revenge. What is a man
If his chief good and market of his time
Be but to sleep and feed? A beast, no more:
Sure he that made us with such large discourse
Looking before and after, gave us not
That capability and god-like reason
To fust in us unused.

occasions = *events, things that happen*
inform = *give the facts against*
spur = *make something or someone go faster*
market = *to make good use of*
discourse = *ability to think clearly*
capability = *ability to do something*
fust = *go bad*

Why then, have I not achieved my purpose?
Why is my murderous uncle still alive?
Am I a coward? Or do I think too much before I act?
Yes, that is my problem.
I want revenge – I have the means and will.
And yet I think too much and still do nothing.
Prince Fortinbras is marching with his men to fight
Over a piece of land. There will be many deaths.
To him, it's a question of his honour; that's his reason.
What excuse do I have then for letting Claudius live?
I have killed a father and accused my mother,
And, in my anger, forgotten my true purpose.
These men march to war, for honour, not for gain.
I will kill too, kill for honour's sake – revenge is the thing
That must fill my heart and mind – to kill the King!

Act 4, Scene 5

[Enter Gertrude and Horatio]
Gertrude: I will not talk to her. My heart's too sad already.
Horatio: Ophelia needs your help and you should pity her.
Gertrude: What is she saying?
Horatio: She speaks about her father and she
mourns his death.
She says strange things we cannot understand.
Yet people listen and are asking questions.
Gertrude: Let her come in then.
[To herself]
Her words will put ideas in bad men's minds.
And make things worse for us.
[Horatio exits and returns with Ophelia. She looks mad and very unhappy]
Ophelia: The lovely Queen of Denmark. Where is she?
Gertrude: Greetings, fair Ophelia.
Ophelia: *[Singing]*
My love is far away. Where has he gone?
Shall I see him again? No, I'm alone.
Gertrude: Poor lady, what do you mean?
Ophelia: *He is dead and gone*
Oh, he is dead and gone.
He is wrapped in white cloth,
Above his grave, a stone.
[Enter Claudius]
Gertrude: Oh, look at this sad sight, my lord.
Ophelia: *Flowers were thrown on his grave*
Watered with my tears.
Claudius: How are you, pretty lady?
Ophelia: I'm well, God help you.
The owl is the bird of death – it has a sad song. They say the

baker's daughter was turned into an owl. Who knows what will happen to any of us? How we are changed!

Claudius: Poor girl, she's thinking of her father's death.

Ophelia: Do not talk of that.

Tomorrow is St Valentine's Day
When I shall see my love,
Who'll open his door
To let in a maid
Who'll soon be a maid no more.

Claudius: Poor, pretty Ophelia.

Ophelia: *These young men are all the same*
They get you in their bed
Then it's the maid who gets the blame
When they refuse to wed.

Claudius: How long has she been like this, poor girl?

Ophelia: Well, we must be patient. But he is in the cold, hard ground.

That makes me so sad. I'll tell my brother – he'll know what to do.

But now it's time to go. Goodbye to you all, goodbye.

[Exit Ophelia]

Claudius: *[To Horatio]*

Follow her. Watch what she does.

[Exit Horatio]

This madness comes from her dear father's death.

But that's not the only thing. Our sorrows crowd upon us

And we are in much danger.

First her father's killed. Then Hamlet has to leave.

The people are all angry and they turn against us.

We tried to hide Polonius' death and that was wrong.

Now mad Ophelia's brother has returned from France.

Everything that's happened, Laertes blames on me.

Oh, Gertrude, I'm attacked on every side. What can I do?

[People are heard shouting, outside the door]
Gertrude: What's all that noise?
Claudius: Where are my soldiers? They must guard the door!
[Enter a courtier]
What is the matter?
Courtier: Save yourself, my lord.
Laertes is here. He's with a crowd of people.
They're armed and angry. They want Laertes as their king.
They cry, 'Laertes shall be King, Laertes King.'
They shout his name and want you dead, my lord.
Gertrude: The fools! How easily they believe false,
wicked lies!
[There is a loud noise]
Claudius: They've broken down the doors!
[Enter Laertes, armed, with a crowd of men behind him]
Laertes: Where is the King? I must see the King!
[The crowd shouts: We must see the King!]
Laertes: *[To the crowd]*
Good friends, I will speak to him alone.
[Exit the crowd of people]
Laertes: *[To Claudius]*
You wicked king, give me back my father!
Gertrude: *[Taking hold of the young man]*
Please calm down, good Laertes.
Laertes: That would insult[74] my father and my mother too.
Claudius: Why have you brought these men here,
good Laertes?
Let him go, dear Gertrude. I do not fear these people.
I am their king and heaven will protect me.
What do you want with me, Laertes?
Laertes: Where is my father?
Claudius: Dead. Killed, but not by me.

Laertes: How did he die? You must tell me the truth.
Whatever happens, I must have revenge!
Claudius: Revenge should be for enemies, not friends.
Do you agree?
Laertes: I do.
Claudius: Then here's the truth. Your father was my friend. I
did not kill him.
[Someone shouts outside: 'Let her come in.']
Laertes: What's happening now?
[Enter Ophelia, carrying flowers and with more flowers in her hair]
Oh God, my sister! Sweet Ophelia! Has she lost her mind?
Can a young girl go mad as easily as an old man dies?
And has she sent her reason to the grave with him?

Laertes: *Dear maid, kind sister, sweet Ophelia:*
O Heavens, is't possible a young maid's wits
Should be as mortal as an old man's life?
Nature is fine in love, and where 'tis fine,
It sends some precious instance of itself
After the thing it loves.

wits = *senses*
mortal = *something that will die*
fine = *made better by*
precious = *valuable*
instance = *small part of*

Ophelia: *[singing]*
The poor old man was carried by –
Hey, nonny, nonny.
And now he in his grave does lie –
Hey, nonny, nonny.
How sad my song is, oh, how sad. Sing it with me.
As the wheel turns,
Down he goes.

Down, down into his grave.
[Ophelia now gives flowers to everyone in turn]
[To Laertes]
This flower is rosemary. It means memory.
And these pansies are sweet thoughts.
Always remember me in your thoughts, my love.
Laertes: Oh, God, I always will.
Ophelia: *[To Claudius]*
Here are your flowers – I think you know their meaning:
One is for flattery[75] and one for ungratefulness[76].
[To Gertrude]
This rue's for you, you must repent in sorrow.
And here's some left for me. That's for my sadness.
A daisy too – that's yours, for you were tricked by lies.
I looked for violets, to show my faithfulness.
But when my father died, they all died too.
So here's a song for him:
Will he ever come again? No, no, he is dead.
He has gone, he has gone.
Pray to God to help him.
And pray for me and for us all. Goodbye.
[Exit Ophelia]
Laertes: Do you see this, oh God?
Claudius: Laertes, believe me. I do share your sadness.
Now you must judge me, find me free from guilt.
If you do not, then all I have is yours –
My crown, my life. If I am freed from blame,
You must be patient and do everything I say.
Laertes: I do agree, but yet I want to know,
How my poor father died, why he was buried secretly.
Claudius: So you shall. The guilty will be punished.
Come with me.
[Exit Claudius and Laertes]

Always remember me in your thoughts, my love.

Act 4, Scene 6

[Enter Horatio and, from the other side, a servant]
Servant: Some sailors brought this letter for you, sir.
Horatio: It must be from Lord Hamlet, let me see it.
[Horatio takes the letter and reads it aloud]
Horatio: *After two days at sea, our ship was chased by pirates[77].*
There was a fight, I jumped onto their ship and could not get
back. The pirates looked after me well – they knew I was a
prince. They must not be punished.
These sailors have letters for the King. See that he gets them.
These sailors know where I am and they will bring you to me.
Come as quickly as you can.
Rosencrantz and Guildenstern are on their way to England
– I'll tell you more about them later. Your friend for ever,
Hamlet.
[To the sailors]
Come, I'll take you to the King. And then we'll find
Prince Hamlet.

Act 4, Scene 7

[Enter Claudius and Laertes]

Claudius: Now that you have heard the truth, I trust we can be friends.
Prince Hamlet killed Polonius, your father.
But Hamlet thought the poor old man was me.

Laertes: I believe that now but do not understand
Why Hamlet was not punished.
He had killed my father and he threatened[78] you.

Claudius: There are two reasons why I did not punish him.
The first – his mother loves him and I myself love her.
Secondly, the people love Prince Hamlet more than me.
And they will blame me, if the prince is harmed.

Laertes: So, my father's dead, and my dear sister's mad.
But I'll have my revenge, be sure of that.

Claudius: And so shall I. I have a plan. Now, listen…

[Enter a servant]

What do you want?

Servant: Letters have come from Hamlet, my good lord.
One is for you. One for the Queen, his mother.

Claudius: *[Very surprised]*
From Hamlet? Give them to me.

[Exit servant]

You shall hear them, good Laertes.

[Claudius reads the letter aloud]

Great king. I am back in Denmark sooner than I thought.
Tomorrow I shall tell you the cause of my sudden strange
return.

I am alone. Hamlet.

What does he mean by this?
And why is he alone?

Have Rosencrantz and Guildenstern returned too?
What do you think, Laertes?
Laertes: I do not know, my lord.
But I long to see him and curse[79] him to his face.
Then my revenge will follow.
Claudius: Of course it will. I have a plan to help you.
You will kill Hamlet. But in such a way,
That everyone will think it was an accident.
Then we will both be safe. What do you think of that?
Laertes: My father's dead and Hamlet must die too.
Tell me your plan.
Claudius: Hamlet will soon be here, but do not talk to him.
Stay in your room, my good friend, Laertes.
I shall tell Hamlet you have returned to Denmark.
Not in revenge, but as a loving brother.
I shall suggest you have some bouts[80] with Hamlet.
You are well-matched and it would be good sport.
I'm sure you'll win, but to be doubly sure,
Fight with a pointed sword – he will not notice.
Then, with the whole court watching, you can kill him.

Claudius: ... *he being remiss,*
Most generous and free from all contriving,
Will not peruse the foils, so that with a little ease,
Or with a little shuffling, you may choose
A sword unbated, and in a pass of practice,
Requite him for your father.

remiss = *not thinking that anything bad will happen*
contriving = *clever planning*
peruse = *look at carefully*
shuffling = *unfair tricks*
unbated = *sharp*
pass of practice = *unfair movement of the sword*
requite = *have revenge on*

No one will blame you for it. What do you think?
Laertes: I have some poison that I bought in France.
I'll put it on my sword – one drop will kill him.
Claudius: Good. I'll lay a bet that you will be the winner.
Now, let me think. Yes, I have a plan.
As the fight goes on, Hamlet will get thirsty.
I'll have wine ready – it will be poisoned too.
When Hamlet drinks – he dies!
[Enter Gertrude. Claudius speaks to her]
So, Gertrude, what's your news?
Gertrude: Soon after one sad death, another follows.
Your sister's drowned, Laertes.
Laertes: Drowned? Where?
Gertrude: She was near a little river, picking flowers,
Singing and sighing for her father's death.
A tree grows there, which leans over the water
And your poor sister put flowers among its branches.
When one branch broke, she fell into the water
Not realizing her danger. For a time,
Her clothes kept her afloat, then, singing softly
She sank beneath the water and was drowned.
Laertes: You say my sister's drowned?
Gertrude: *[Crying]*
Drowned, drowned.
Laertes: Oh, fair Ophelia, I'm trying not to cry –
No more water, you are drowned already.
Goodbye, my lord. My heart was full of anger,
Which these sad tears have cooled – but not for long.
My anger will return.
[Exit Laertes]
Claudius: *[To Gertrude]*
We must follow him, my queen, my dearest Gertrude.
It took me a long time to calm him down.

Your sister's drowned, Laertes.

Now he'll soon be in a rage again.
Come with me, Gertrude.
[Exit Claudius and Gertrude]

Act 5, Scene 1

[A graveyard[81], near the castle. A grave-digger[82] is digging a grave. He is singing happily]

[Enter Hamlet and Horatio. They are wearing long cloaks[83]]

Hamlet: He sings as he digs a grave! This fellow must enjoy his work.

I'll speak to him. Whose grave is this?

Grave-digger: Mine, sir.

Hamlet: *[Laughing]*

I suppose it is, as you are digging it.

What man will be buried in the grave?

Grave-digger: No man, sir.

Hamlet: What woman, then?

Grave-digger: No woman either, sir.

Hamlet: Then tell me, who will be buried in this grave?

Grave-digger: Someone who was a woman, sir, but now, alas, she's dead.

Hamlet: *[To Horatio]*

This man is very careful with his words, Horatio.

You'd think he was a courtier, the way he talks!

[To the grave-digger]

How long have you been a grave-digger?

Grave-digger: Well, I'll never forget my first day at work. It was the same day that old King Hamlet won the battle against King Fortinbras of Norway.

Hamlet: How long ago was that?

Grave-digger: How long ago? *[He laughs]* Every fool knows that! It was the day that young Hamlet was born. He's mad, you know and has been sent to England.

Hamlet: Why was he sent to England?

Grave-digger: Because he's mad. They're all mad there, you know.

Hamlet: How long does a man's body take to rot[84]?
Grave-digger: That depends, sir. Some bodies are rotten before they are buried! But eight or nine years is the usual time. A tanner[85] will last nine years.
Hamlet: Why will a tanner last longer?
Grave-digger: Because his skin is tanned by his trade. That keeps out the water.
[He picks up a skull[86] and holds it up]
This skull has been in the ground for more than twenty years. It belonged to another mad fellow – Yorick, the old King's jester[87].
Hamlet: Give it to me.
[He holds the skull and looks at it sadly]
Alas, poor Yorick. I knew him, Horatio.
He often played with me when I was very young.
He was always smiling as he made his jokes.
Poor fellow, he's not smiling now!
There's no escape, Horatio.
A woman paints her face to keep her beauty.
But she'll still end like this.
Great Alexander ruled the world and Caesar governed Rome.
Now both are dust and all their power has gone.
[He puts down the skull]
[Enter Claudius, Gertrude, Laertes and a priest. Courtiers are carrying an open coffin with a body in it]
The King and Queen here? And Ophelia's brother?
Whose funeral is this? Let's hide and listen.
[The open coffin is put into the grave, which is wide and shallow]
Laertes: *[To the priest]*
Are there no more prayers to say? No more holy songs to sing?
Priest: We have already done too much. She has her wreaths[88] and flowers.

Alas, poor Yorick. I knew him, Horatio.

Her coffin has been placed in holy ground.
But there is still a doubt about her death.
She may have killed herself. If that is true,
Then she is damned for ever.
Laertes: Damned? No, my sister's gone to heaven.
It's you who will be damned you cursed priest!
Hamlet: *[Quietly]*
His sister? Is this the fair Ophelia?
Gertrude: *[Throwing flowers in the grave]*
Sweet flowers for a sweet lady.
I had hoped to see you as my Hamlet's bride
And thrown these flowers upon your marriage-bed.
Not on your grave.
Laertes: Oh, three times cursed be that man whose
wicked deed
Caused you to lose your reason!

Gertrude: *Sweets to the sweet, farewell.*
I hoped thou shouldst have been my Hamlet's wife:
I thought thy bride-bed to have decked, sweet maid
And not have strewed thy grave.
Laertes: *O treble woe,*
Fall ten times treble on that cursed head
Whose wicked deed thy most ingenious sense
Deprived thee of.

bride-bed = *the bed of a newly-married woman*
decked = *made beautiful*
strewed = *covered*
treble = *three times*
woe = *deep sadness*
ingenious sense = *ability to think*
deprived = *took away from*

My sweetest sister, I must hold you in my arms again!

[Laertes jumps down into the grave and takes Ophelia in his arms]
Cover us both with earth and I'll die with her!
[Hamlet steps forward]
Hamlet: What right have you to call on heaven and earth
To see your sorrow? This is I, Hamlet the Dane!
[Hamlet jumps into the grave with Laertes]
Laertes: *[Putting his hands round Hamlet's throat]*
The devil take your soul!
Hamlet: Take your hands away!
I am not often angry, but when I am – beware!
Take your hands away I said!
Claudius: Separate them! Stop them fighting!
Gertrude: Hamlet, Hamlet!
Horatio: Calm yourself, my lord.
Hamlet: I'll fight him to the death about this matter!
Gertrude: What matter's that, my son?
Hamlet: I loved Ophelia – more than forty
thousand brothers!
What would you do for her, Laertes?
Claudius: Oh, he is mad, Laertes.
Gertrude: For the love of God – separate them!
Hamlet: I asked you what you would do for her.
Give me your answer! Would you fight with me?
Cry, starve[89] yourself or tear yourself to pieces?
Drink vinegar, eat a crocodile? I don't think so.
You say that you will die with her – then so will I!
Let them throw earth on both of us and bury us alive!
Promise anything you like – I can do better!
Gertrude: This is a fit of madness. It will pass.
Then he'll be quiet again.
Hamlet: *[Speaking more calmly, to Laertes]*
Why do you curse me, sir? I've always loved you.

The devil take your soul!

But what has happened, had to be, that's all.
[Exit Hamlet]
Claudius: Good Horatio, please look after him.
[Exit Horatio]
Dear Gertrude, see that your mad son is watched.
Laertes, the things we planned last night, must
happen quickly.
This grave will be remembered by another death,
Then we'll wait patiently for quieter times.

Act 5, Scene 2

[Enter Hamlet and Horatio]

Hamlet: You know that I escaped. Now here's what happened.

Horatio: Please tell me everything, my lord.

Hamlet: I was on the ship to England and I could not sleep.
Instead of thinking, I decided on some action.
Sudden decisions sometimes help us more than plans.
And God protects us, whatever path we follow.

Horatio: That, sir, is very true.

Hamlet: Then listen.
I covered up my face, went to the other cabin,
Where Rosencrantz and Guildenstern were sleeping.
I found the letter that the King had written
And took it to my cabin.
There I unsealed[90] it and read these wicked words.
The English king was told I was a traitor,
And that I should be killed, without delay.

Horatio: How terrible! How did you save yourself?
What did you do?

Hamlet: I wrote another letter with a different order:
My two companions should be put to death
So what was meant to be my fate, was theirs.

Horatio: How did you seal this letter, my good lord?

Hamlet: I had my father's ring upon my finger
With the royal seal of Denmark on it.
I sealed the letter with the ring and put it back.
The next day we were attacked by pirates. The rest you know.

Horatio: So Rosencrantz and Guilderstern went to
their deaths.

Hamlet: They plotted[91] mine, I'm sure they did. Do not feel
sorry for them.

They spied on me and did the King's work for him.
Horatio: How wicked Claudius is!
Hamlet: Wicked enough to die like the mad dog he is.
He killed the King, my father, didn't he?
My mother's now his whore; he tried to kill me too.
And now he's king of Denmark, destroying every hope I had
Of ruling like my father.
I have cause enough to kill him, don't you agree?
Horatio: Then you must do it quickly, before an answer
comes from England. The time is short, you know it.
Hamlet: Short as a man's life, Horatio, and ended in a minute.
But I'm sorry that I fought Laertes. His sorrows are like mine.
I lost my temper. Let's hope we can be friends again.
Horatio: Quiet. Who's this coming?
[Enter Osric, a young courtier. He is dressed in the latest fashion]
Osric: *[He takes off his hat and bows]*
Welcome back to Denmark, my good lord.
Hamlet: Do you know this smart young man, Horatio?
Horatio: No, my good lord.
Hamlet: You are lucky, then. He is the King's friend,
that's for sure.
Osric: I have a message from the King, my lord. It is for you.
Hamlet: Then tell me what it is. And put your hat back on
your head.
Osric: Then here's the message. You know sir, that Laertes
has been in France, but has just returned to Denmark.
He's a fine gentleman, who is very popular.
Hamlet: Go on, I know him well.
Osric: In France, Laertes is well-known for his skill with a
sword and he has won many bouts there. Now, he'd like a
friendly fight with you.
Hamlet: What is his weapon, sir?

Osric: Sword and dagger, my good lord.
Hamlet: *[Smiling]*
That's two weapons! But I'll fight him.
Osric: The King has made a bet, sir, and he is backing you.
His stake[92] is six fine horses. Laertes has bet six silver swords.
If Laertes wins, then he will get the horses.
If you win, sir, the king will get the swords and horses too.
Hamlet: Very well. How many bouts? Nine? That's the usual.
Osric: There will be twelve, sir. A hit ends the bout, of course.
To win the match, Laertes must score three more
hits than you.
Hamlet: I agree. I think that I can beat him.
When do we fight?
Osric: All things are ready, sir, if you are ready too.
Hamlet: Then tell the King I'm ready.
Osric: I will, my lord.
[Exit Osric]
Horatio: I think that you will lose this bet, my good lord.
Hamlet: I do not think so.
I have been practising and I am fit.
If Laertes scores no more than eight hits, I shall win.
Horatio: I hope you will, my good lord.
Hamlet: And yet my heart is sad – I don't know why.
I feel that something bad may happen.
Horatio: Then don't fight. I'll make your excuses
to the King.
Hamlet: No, no. We are in God's hands, as all things are.
I can't foretell[93] the future, no man can.
Death will come sometime – if not now, then later.
We must be ready for it, that is all.
*[Hamlet and Horatio go into the Great Hall. Enter Claudius,
Gertrude, Laertes and all the courtiers. There are swords and*

daggers ready and some wine on a table. Claudius takes Laertes'
hand in his. Hamlet holds out his hand]
Claudius: Come, Hamlet, come and take Laertes' hand.
Hamlet: *[To Laertes]*
Pardon me, good sir, my actions harmed you,
But as you know sir, I have not been myself.
The wrongs I've done you, have come from my madness.

> **Hamlet:** *Give me your pardon sir, I've done you wrong,*
> *But pardon it as you are a gentleman.*
> *This presence knows,*
> *And you must needs have heard how I am punished*
> *With sore distraction? What I have done*
> *That might your nature, honour and exception*
> *Roughly awake, I here proclaim was madness.*
>
> **presence** = *all the people now here*
> **sore** = *very bad*
> **distraction** = *unhappy confusion, madness*
> **nature** = *true feelings*
> **exception** = *disapproval*
> **proclaim** = *say clearly*

That madness was my enemy and made me yours.
Sir, before these people I tell you I am sorry.
My actions hurt your family by mistake.
Laertes: Your words satisfy[94] my feelings, do believe it.
But not my honour. Wiser men must judge you.
Until then, I accept your love with kindness.
Hamlet: Then we will fight as brothers, though your skills
Will far surpass mine and I know it.
Laertes: You are joking, sir.
Hamlet: No, sir, indeed I'm not.
Claudius: Give them the swords, young Osric.
You know the bet, Hamlet?
Hamlet: Yes, sir, I do. I hope you will not lose it.

Claudius: I don't think so. I know you both play well.
[Hamlet and Laertes choose their weapons]
Laertes: This sword's too heavy. Let me try another one.
Hamlet: This one suits me well. Are these swords all the same length?
Osric: Yes, my good lord.
[Hamlet and Laertes get ready to fight]
Claudius: Put cups of wine ready on this table.
If Hamlet wins the first and second bouts
Or if he hits Laertes in the third, then let the great guns fire!
Now the King drinks to Hamlet – his skill and his success!
Let music sound – the trumpets and the drums.
[Claudius drinks]
Now let the great guns roar – success to Hamlet!
[Claudius drinks. Sound of music and guns]
Here is a pearl, the finest that I have.
I'll put it in this silver cup when Hamlet drinks.
It is a great king's gift to his most noble son.
Now, judges, are you ready? Then let the fight begin!
Hamlet: Come on, sir!
Laertes: Come on, my lord!
[They fight]
Hamlet: One! The first hit is mine.
Laertes: No hit.
Hamlet: Let the judge speak.
Osric: A hit, a clear one.
Laertes: Right. The next bout, then.
Claudius: Wait. Here is the pearl, I've put it in the cup.
Dear Hamlet, drink. This pearl is yours!
[Claudius drops the poisoned pearl into the cup of wine]
Here, Hamlet, take the cup and drink!
Hamlet: I'll play this next bout first.
[They fight]

That's another hit. I know I'm right.
Laertes: That was your second hit, I do agree.
Claudius: Gertrude, our son will win!
Gertrude: He's hot and out of breath. Here, Hamlet
Take my handkerchief and wipe your face.
I drink to your good fortune, Hamlet!
[Gertrude picks up the poisoned cup]
Hamlet: Thank you for your good wishes, madam.
Claudius: Do not drink, Gertrude!
Gertrude: I must drink to my son.
[She drinks and then walks up to Hamlet]
Claudius: *[To himself]*
It is the poisoned cup. Nothing can save her now.
Hamlet: I dare not drink yet, madam.
Gertrude: Then let me wipe your face.
Laertes: *[To Claudius]*
My lord, I'll hit him now.
Claudius: I don't think so.
Laertes: *[To himself]*
I am almost sorry that I planned to kill him.
Hamlet: Come on, Laertes. It's the third bout.
I don't believe you're trying.
Don't make a fool of me.
Laertes: Come on, attack me then!
[They fight]
Osric: No hit on either side.
Laertes: Take that!
[He wounds Hamlet with his poisoned sword]
[The two men fight very hard. Laertes' sword is knocked from his hand by Hamlet. Hamlet picks up Laertes' sword and wounds him with it]
Claudius: Separate them! They are out of control!
Hamlet: No. I have just begun to fight. [He gives his own sword to Laertes]*

Come on, sir.
[They fight again]
[Gertrude falls to the ground]
Osric: The Queen is ill. Help her.
Horatio: Both men are bleeding now.
How are you, my lord Hamlet?
Osric: And how are you, Laertes? Are you badly hurt?
Laertes: Caught in my own trap.
Osric – my sword was poisoned.
Hamlet: What's wrong with the Queen?
Claudius: She has fainted at the sight of blood.
Gertrude: No, no. It was the drink, dear Hamlet, the drink.
The drink was poisoned.
[She dies]
Hamlet: This is that villain's work! Lock all the doors.
No one must escape. Seek out the traitor!
[Laertes falls to the ground]
Laertes: The traitor is the King.
Hamlet, you are dying, poisoned by my sword.
Nothing can save you now. My fate's the same
And my own wickedness has killed me too.
Your mother has been poisoned by the drink.
The King's to blame for everything – I can say no more.
Hamlet: The sword is poisoned?
Then I'll turn the point on him!
[Hamlet stabs Claudius with Laertes' sword]
All: Treason! Treason!
Claudius: Oh, help me friends. I am only wounded.
Hamlet: Will it take more to kill you?
Then drink this poisoned wine, you murderous, evil villain.
Follow my mother to your death, you damned Dane.
[Claudius dies]
Laertes: He is killed by his own poison.
Oh, forgive me, Hamlet,

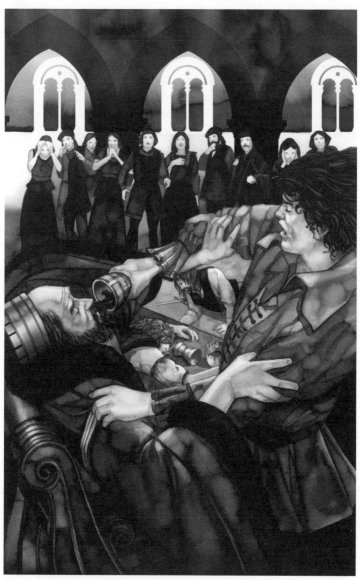

'Follow my mother to your death, you damned Dane.'

As I forgive you. The blame is not yours, but his.
[Laertes dies]
Hamlet: Heaven forgive me too.
I follow you to death, Laertes.
Goodbye to you, unhappy queen. Help me, Horatio,
I am dying.
[Hamlet speaks to all the courtiers]
You who have watched these terrible events,
But have not understood them, are now all pale with fear.
I would tell you everything, but I have no time.
Death will not give me time to speak.
I am dying, Horatio,
But you must live to tell all men the truth.
Horatio: I cannot live when you are dead, dear lord.
There's still some poisoned wine left in this cup –
I'll drink it now and follow you to death.
[He picks up the cup]
Hamlet: *[Taking the cup from him]*
No, give the cup to me. You must not drink.
Stay in this sad world. Turn from the joys of heaven.
You are my only friend and you must tell my story.
[There is the sound of guns and war-like music]
What is that noise?
Osric: Young Fortinbras has returned from Poland,
Where he won the battle. And together with him,
Are messengers from England.
Hamlet: I shall not live to see them.
I am nearly dead, Horatio.
And with my dying voice I name Prince Fortinbras
As the next king of Denmark. Tell him my story, Horatio.
No more words from me. The rest is silence.
[Hamlet dies]
Horatio: There ends a noble life. Good night, sweet prince.
And may God's angels carry you to heaven.

[Enter Fortinbras, his soldiers and the messengers from England]
Fortinbras: What has happened here?
Horatio: More dreadful things than you have ever seen.
Fortinbras: Oh, Death, you are the winner here.
What noble prizes have you taken?
Messenger: I had a message for the King, but I have
come too late
To tell him Rosencrantz and Guildenstern are dead.
Horatio: Not by the King's wish.
I have seen many things: murder of kings and princes,
Death caused by accident and unnatural acts.
All I shall tell.
Fortinbras: And I long to hear it.
I think that I can claim this kingdom as my own.
Horatio: That was Lord Hamlet's dying wish.
Let these dead bodies be shown to the people,
For they must know the truth and that will calm them.
Fortinbras: Let four captains carry Hamlet to a resting-place.
So all can see him. He was a noble prince
And would have made a fine king, if he'd lived.
These awful deaths have made this place a battlefield
And not a royal court. Soldiers! Fire your guns to
Honour Denmark's noble prince.
And play sad music in his memory!
*[Soldiers carry out Hamlet's body, to the sound of music. The
great guns are fired]*

Points for Understanding

Act 1

1 Horatio thought that the Ghost was a warning.
  Why did he think this?
2 Why did Horatio decide to tell Hamlet about the Ghost?
3 How did Hamlet feel about
  (a) his dead father
  (b) his mother and
  (c) Claudius?
4 Laertes and Polonius gave Ophelia some advice. What was it?
5 How did Ophelia react to their advice?

Act 2

1 Describe Hamlet's strange behaviour. What did Ophelia and her father think had caused it?
2 Why had Claudius sent for Hamlet's friends, Rosencrantz and Guildenstern?
3 Do you think that Hamlet was mad or not in this scene? (Scene 2) Explain your answer.
4 Hamlet had a plan. What was it and what did he want to prove?

Act 3

1 How was Hamlet feeling before he saw Ophelia?
  How do you know?
2 Do you think that Hamlet was unkind to Ophelia in this scene? (Scene 1)
  How can you explain his behaviour?
3 Why did Hamlet hate women so much?
4 Claudius and Polonius had different explanations for Hamlet's actions. What were they and what did they plan to do about him?
5 What happened when Claudius watched the play?
6 Why didn't Hamlet kill Claudius when he saw him praying?
7 Why was Gertrude sure that Hamlet was mad by the end of this scene? (Scene 4)

Act 4

1 What did Claudius now plan to do to protect himself?
2 Hamlet saw Prince Fortinbras and his army. How did his feelings change after that?
3 How had Ophelia changed? What had happened to her?
4 Why had Laertes returned to Denmark and what did he plan to do?
5 How did Claudius get Laertes to change his mind?
6 Hamlet sent a letter to Horatio. What did it tell him?
7 With Laertes' help, Claudius planned the death of Hamlet. What was the plan?
8 What sad news did Gertrude have for them?

Act 5

1 Hamlet is a tragedy, but the grave-digger is a comic character. Why did Shakespeare want to make his audience laugh in this scene?
2 Why did Laertes and Hamlet fight in Ophelia's grave?
3 What happened to Rosencrantz and Guildenstern? Do you feel sorry for them?
4 Who died in this scene and how? (Scene 2)
5 Who lived to tell the true story?
6 Who was going to be the next king of Denmark?

Glossary

1 **influenced** – *to influence* (page 5)
   to affect the way that someone thinks or behaves, or to affect the
   way that something happens.
2 **manuscript** (page 5)
   a writer's original pages of a book, article, or document before it is
   published.
3 **treason** (page 5)
   the crime of helping your country's enemies or of trying to destroy
   your country's government.
4 **retired** – *to retire* (page 5)
   to stop working, especially when you reach the age when you are
   officially too old to work.
5 **fate** (page 6)
   the things that happen to someone, especially unpleasant things.
6 **uneasy** (page 6)
   someone who feels *uneasy* feels slightly nervous, worried, or upset
   about something. This nervous and worried feeling is called *unease*.
7 **revenge** (page 6)
   something that you do to hurt or punish someone because they
   have hurt you or someone else.
8 **unique** (page 7)
   very special, unusual, or good.
9 **battlements** (page 10)
   a wall around the top of a castle, with spaces through which
   weapons could be fired.
10 **guard duty** – *to be on guard duty* (page 10)
   to be officially put somewhere to guard someone or something.
11 **armour** (page 10)
   metal clothing that soldiers wore in the middle ages to protect their
   bodies.
12 **state** (page 11)
   a country, or its government.
13 **cock** (page 11)
   an adult male chicken. The noise that a cock makes is called
   crowing. Cocks crow in the morning, when the sun rises.

14 *courtier* (page 12)
someone who has an official position at the court of a king or
queen, or who spends time there.

15 *sorrow* (page 12)
great sadness.

16 *mourned* – *to mourn someone* (page 12)
to feel extremely sad because someone has died, and to express this
in public.

17 *gracious* (page 12)
showing kindness and good manners.

18 *coronation* (page 12)
a ceremony at which someone officially becomes king or queen.

19 *grief* (page 14)
a strong feeling of sadness, usually because someone has died.

20 *honour* (page 14)
honour is the respect that people have for someone who achieves
something great, is very powerful, or behaves in a way that is
morally right. If you *honour* someone you show your respect or
admiration for them.

21 *forbids* – *to forbid something* (page 14)
to tell someone that they must not do something.

22 *widow* (page 15)
a woman whose husband has died and who has not married again.

23 *whore* (page 15)
an insulting word for a *prostitute* – a woman who has sex with
people for money.

24 *funeral* (page 15)
a ceremony that takes place after someone dies, usually including a
religious ceremony, and the formal process of taking the body to the
place where it is buried.

25 *chastity* (page 16)
an old word meaning the condition of someone who has not had
sex. Laertes is warning Ophelia that Hamlet wants to have sex with
her.

26 *blessing* (page 16)
permission or support for something.

27 *custom* (page 18)
something that people do that is traditional or usual.

28 **reputation** (page 18)
the opinion that people have that a person, place, or thing is good.
29 **tomb** (page 18)
the place where a dead person is buried, especially one consisting of a large stone structure.
30 **beckons** – *to beckon to someone* (page 20)
to signal to someone to come towards you.
31 **traitor** (page 20)
someone who is not loyal to their friends, family, employer, or country.
32 **tricked** – *to trick someone* (page 20)
to make someone believe something that is not true.
33 **deceived** – *to deceive someone* (page 20)
to trick someone by behaving in a dishonest way.
34 **sin** (page 20)
an action, thought, or way of behaving that is wrong according to religious laws.
35 **conscience** (page 21)
the ideas and feelings you have that tell you whether something you are doing is right or wrong.
36 **accuse** (page 21)
to say that someone has done something wrong or committed a crime.
37 **villain** (page 21)
an evil person, or a criminal.
38 **sworn** – *to swear something* (page 21)
to promise to do something. Hamlet has *sworn revenge* – he has promised to punish Claudius for murdering his father.
39 **noble** – (page 21)
behaving in an honest and brave way that other people admire. The expression *my noble lord* was used in the past for talking formally to a member of the royal family.
40 **reveal** (page 21)
to let something become known, for example a secret or information that was previously not known.
41 **fair** (page 27)
beautiful. *Fair* is usually only used with this meaning in stories or poems.

42 **fishmonger** (page 27)

someone whose job is to sell fish. In Shakespeare's time, *fishmonger* was a slang word used to describe a man who was in charge of a *brothel* – a place where men pay to have sex with prostitutes. Hamlet is insulting Polonius.

43 **players** (page 30)

player is an old word meaning 'actor'. A group of actors have come to give a performance.

44 **coward** (page 31)

someone who is not brave enough to fight or do something difficult or dangerous that they should do.

45 **dagger** (page 31)

a weapon like a very small sword.

46 **devil** (page 31)

an evil spirit.

47 **whipped** – *to whip* (page 32)

to hit someone with a *whip* – a long thin piece of leather with a handle on one end. Claudius says that Hamlet has *whipped* his conscience. This means that he has made him start to feel guilty for what he has done.

48 **deed** (page 33)

something that someone does.

49 **tapestry** (page 33)

a thick heavy cloth that has pictures or patterns woven into it. *Tapestries* are often hung on walls.

50 **damn** (page 37)

to cause someone to go to hell. Someone who is going to go to hell is *damned*.

51 **bet** (page 40)

to risk an amount of money by saying what you think will happen or has happened. You lose the money if you are wrong and win more if you are right.

52 **spies** – *spy* (page 41)

someone who watches someone secretly so that you know everything that they do.

53 **wound** (page 41)

if someone is wounded, they are injured by something that damages their skin or flesh, especially severely.

54 **sword** (page 43)
a weapon with a short handle and a long sharp blade.
55 **ashamed** – *I'm ashamed to say* (page 45)
someone who is ashamed feels guilty and embarrassed because they
have done something wrong or have not reached a standard that
people expect. *I'm ashamed to say* is used for admitting something
that you think people might be surprised or disappointed about.
56 **mockery** – *to make a mockery of something* (page 45)
to make someone or something seem stupid or useless.
57 **vows** (page 45)
a set of promises that people make to each other. The *vows* made
during a wedding ceremony are called *marriage vows*.
58 **lust** (page 45)
a strong feeling of wanting to have sex.
59 **portrait** (page 45)
a painting, drawing, or photograph of someone, especially of their
face only.
60 **incest** (page 45)
sexual activity between people who are closely related, such as a
brother and sister.
61 **thief** (page 46)
someone who steals something. An instance of stealing something
is called a *theft*.
62 **chide** (page 46)
to criticize someone, or to speak to them in an angry way because
you think their behaviour is wrong. This word is mainly used in
stories and poems.
63 **disobedient** (page 46)
someone who deliberately does the opposite of what someone in
authority has told them to do, or deliberately disobeys rules.
64 **repent** (page 46)
to recognize that you have done something wrong and to feel
ashamed and sorry about it, especially when you have done
something against the rules of your religion.
65 **confess** (page 46)
to admit that you have done something wrong.
66 **rage** (page 48)
a very strong feeling of anger.

67 *chapel* (page 48)
a small church, or a special room used as a church, where Christians can pray or worship.

68 *concealed* – *to conceal something* (page 48)
to hide something so that it cannot be found.

69 *dismay* (page 48)
the feeling of being very worried, disappointed, or sad about something surprising or shocking that has happened.

70 *maggot* – *maggots and worms* (page 51)
a small soft creature with no arms or legs that later changes into a fly. Maggots are found in old meat and dead bodies. *Worms* are similar creatures that live in the earth. Hamlet is saying that Polonius is dead and will soon be eaten by the creatures that live under the ground.

71 *dread* (page 51)
fear of something bad that might happen or that is going to happen.

72 *seeks* – *to seek something* (page 52)
to ask for something, or to try to get something.

73 *march* (page 52)
if soldiers march, they walk in a group with each person matching the speed and movements of the others.

74 *insult* (page 56)
to say or do something offensive.

75 *flattery* (page 58)
praise that is not sincere but is intended to get you something that you want.

76 *ungratefulness* (page 58)
if you are *grateful*, you want to thank someone because they have given you something or have done something for you. *Ungratefulness* is behaviour or attitudes that show you are not grateful, especially when other people think you should be grateful.

77 *pirate* (page 60)
someone who attacks ships while they are sailing in order to steal things from them.

78 *threatened* – *to threaten someone* (page 61)
to tell someone that you might or you will cause them harm, especially in order to make them do something.

79 *curse* (page 62)
to say or think offensive or impolite words about someone or something.

80 **bout** (page 62)
a fight with swords as a sport or entertainment.

81 **graveyard** (page 66)
an area of land where dead people are buried, usually around a church.

82 **gravedigger** (page 66)
someone whose job is to use a tool to make the hole in the earth that dead people are buried in.

83 **cloak** (page 66)
a long thick loose coat without sleeves, that fastens around your neck.

84 **rot** (page 67)
to be gradually destroyed as a result of a natural process of change. Something that has been destroyed in this way is *rotten*.

85 **tanner** (page 67)
someone whose job is to make animal skins into leather.

86 **skull** (page 67)
the bones of the head.

87 **jester** (page 67)
someone in the past whose job was to entertain an important person by saying and doing funny things.

88 **wreath** (page 67)
a circle of flowers or leaves that you put on a grave to show that you are remembering the dead person.

89 **starve** – to starve yourself (page 70)
to kill yourself by not eating enough food.

90 **unsealed** – to unseal (page 73)
to open a letter or document.

91 **plotted** – to plot (page 73)
to make a secret plan with other people to do something bad.

92 **stake** (page 75)
an amount of money that you risk losing when you try to guess the result of a race or competition.

93 **foretell** (page 75)
to say what will happen in the future.

94 **satisfy** (page 76)
to please someone by giving them something that they want or need.

Dictionary extracts adapted from the Macmillan English Dictionary © Macmillan Publishers Limited 2002.

Exercises

Background information

Choose the correct information to complete the sentences.

1 Shakespeare was born in (England) / America.

2 Shakespeare <u>went / didn't go</u> to university.

3 Shakespeare spent a lot of his life in <u>London / Cambridge</u>.

4 Shakespeare worked as <u>a journalist / an actor</u> before he became a playwright.

5 'Hamlet' was written in <u>1599 / 1699</u>.

6 Shakespeare's 'Hamlet' <u>was / wasn't</u> a completely new story.

7 There were about <u>5 / 500</u> theatres in London at that time.

8 Most of the audience at the theatres <u>stood / sat down</u> in those days.

True or False?

Read the statements about Hamlet. Write T (True) or F (False).

1	Hamlet's father was the King of Denmark.	T
2	Hamlet is Claudius' uncle.	
3	Hamlet's mother is still sad about her husband's death.	
4	Hamlet is the first person to see his father's ghost.	
5	Hamlet is not sure whether to believe the ghost.	
6	Hamlet tells his friends, Rosencrantz and Guildenstern, everything.	
7	Hamlet tells the players what story to act.	
8	Hamlet doesn't trust women.	
9	Hamlet's closest friend is Laertes.	
10	Hamlet kills Polonius by accident.	

11 Hamlet fights Laertes at Ophelia's funeral.	
12 Hamlet is responsible for the deaths of Rosencrantz and Guildenstern.	
13 Hamlet and Claudius have a friendly sword fight.	
14 Hamlet kills Claudius.	
15 Hamlet becomes King of Denmark.	

People in the Story

Write each name next to the correct information below.

Hamlet   Gertrude   Polonius   Claudius   Ophelia   Laertes
Prince Fortinbras   Horatio

1		returns from France to get revenge for his father's death.
2		is in love with Hamlet.
3		becomes King of Denmark when Claudius dies.
4		is sent to England but returns.
5		married his brother's wife.
6		is accidentally killed when she drinks poisoned wine.
7		tells Hamlet about the ghost.
8		tells the King that Hamlet is in love.

Multiple Choice

Tick the best answer.

1 Why does Horatio return to Denmark?
  a To go to the funeral of King Hamlet. ✓
  b To see the ghost of King Hamlet.
  c To help his friend, Hamlet.
  d To become King of Denmark.

2 What does Hamlet promise to do for his father's ghost?
  a To tell the Queen the truth.
  b To get revenge.
  c To kill Polonius.
  d To marry Ophelia.

3 Why doesn't Hamlet trust Rosencrantz and Guildenstern?
  a Because they have caused him problems in the past.
  b Because they tell lies.
  c Because they are working for Claudius.
  d Because they do not believe his ghost story.

4 Why does Hamlet rewrite part of the play?
  a To see how Claudius will react.
  b To make Claudius angry.
  c To make his mother upset.
  d To show Ophelia the truth.

5 What is Polonius doing when he is killed?
  a Fighting Hamlet.
  b Hiding in the Queen's room.
  c Defending the King.
  d Talking to Rosencrantz and Guildenstern.

6 Why doesn't Claudius kill Hamlet himself?
  a Because he thinks he might lose the fight.
  b Because he is worried that Hamlet will tell everyone the truth.
  c Because he feels bad about what he has done.
  d Because Hamlet is popular in Denmark.

7 How does Claudius plan to kill Hamlet?
  a He plans to send him on a ship to England and have him killed
    by pirates.
  b He has asked Rosencrantz and Guildenstern to kill him on the ship.
  c He has asked the King of England to kill him when he arrives
    in England.
  d He has told Prince Fortinbras that Hamlet is plotting to kill him.

8 Why does Ophelia go mad?
  a Because Hamlet has left.
  b Because her brother has left.
  c Because her father is dead.
  d Because she has seen a ghost.

9 How does Hamlet get off the ship to England?
  a He jumps onto another ship during a fight.
  b He jumps into the sea and is found by sailors.
  c He tells Rosencrantz and Guildenstern that he is in danger and they
    help him.
  d He speaks to the ship's captain.

10 How does Claudius find out about Hamlet's return to Denmark?
  a Horatio tells him.
  b Rosencrantz and Guildenstern tell him.
  c He receives a letter from Hamlet.
  d Hamlet appears at Ophelia's funeral.

11 Why do Laertes and Hamlet fight at Ophelia's funeral?
  a Because Hamlet thinks that Laertes is working for Claudius.
  b Because Hamlet wants to say goodbye to Ophelia.
  c Because Hamlet is confused.
  d Because Hamlet thinks he is sadder than Laertes about Ophelia's
    death.

12 Who is still alive at the end of the play?
    a Hamlet and Horatio.
    b Hamlet and Laertes.
    c Horatio and Laertes.
    d Horatio and Prince Fortinbras.

Hamlet meets his father's ghost

Look at the picture on the next page. Then underline the correct words.

1 The ghost appears in the castle / <u>on the castle battlements</u>.

2 King Hamlet returns dressed as a soldier / in royal clothes to terrify / make peace with the living.

3 Hamlet's father beckons / speaks to him then walks away.

4 The ghost tells Hamlet the truth / lies about his death / murder.

5 Hamlet's father died a fast / slow death from a poison poured into his ear / cup of wine.

6 Claudius's love of Gertrude / power made him murder his brother.

7 Hamlet feels his mother has been foolish / clever.

8 Hamlet swears to accuse / have revenge for his father's death.

Words from the Story

Complete the gaps. Use each word in the box once.

| marching | tricks | coward | accuses | armour | funeral |
| custom | wounded | plots | fate |

1 The ghost of King Hamlet appears wearing the .... that he wore in battle when he was alive.

2 Hamlet is partly responsible for Ophelia's ....

3 Horatio came to Denmark to attend King Hamlet's ....

4 There is a Danish .... that every time the King drinks, music is played.

5 Claudius .... the people of Denmark into believing that King Hamlet died naturally.

6 Hamlet .... Claudius of killing his father with poison.

7 When Hamlet sees the soldiers .... to fight for land, it reminds him of his purpose.

8 Hamlet is worried that people will think he is a .... for not killing Claudius.

9 Claudius .... to send Hamlet to England and for Hamlet to be killed there.

10 Hamlet is .... by Laertes and dies because the sword is poisoned.

Vocabulary and grammar

Rewrite sentences using the words in capitals.

Example:	BOUT	Claudius suggests a friendly fight between Laertes and Hamlet.
		Claudius suggests Laertes has some bouts with Hamlet.

1	CONSCIENCE	King Hamlet thinks that Gertrude's thoughts and feelings are enough punishment for her.
		King Hamlet thinks
2	MEMORIES	Hamlet tells his father that he will remember him and his story and everything else will fade.
		Hamlet tells his father
3	REVEAL	Hamlet tells Horatio and Marcellus to keep the ghost's visit to the battlements a secret.
		Horatio, Marcellus and Hamlet
4	DREAD	Claudius lives in fear of Hamlet because the people love him.
		Claudius
5	ARMOUR	The ghost was dressed as a soldier.
		King Hamlet
6	MOURN	All Denmark was full of sadness when King Hamlet died.
		All Denmark
7	WOUND	Hamlet swears not to kill his mother, but the truth will hurt her.
		Hamlet swears not to kill his mother

8	COMFORT	The ghost tells Hamlet to make Gertrude feel less sad and worried.
		Hamlet is told

Vocabulary: Verbs and nouns

Match the verbs with the nouns and write them next to the definition.

VERB	NOUN
become follow send ~~tell~~ bet make change overcome	~~the truth~~ a custom a problem your mind a promise king a gift a thousand pounds

1	_tell the truth_	the opposite of when you lie
2		when you say that you will do something for someone
3		give someone a present, usually by post
4		change your opinion or decision
5		do what is traditional
6		to find an answer to a difficult situation
7		what happens to a Prince when his father dies
8		when you put money on a result, usually of a competition

Grammar: Passive verb forms

Write the verb in brackets in the correct passive form.

1 'Hamlet' ......*was written*...... (write) by Shakespeare.

2 Hamlet didn't know that his father .... (poison) by his brother.

3 The ghost of King Hamlet .... first .... (see) by the guards.

4 Hamlet cannot choose his wife. The wives of princes .... (chose) for them.

5 If Claudius had been hiding in the room, he .... (kill) by Hamlet.

6 Claudius thinks that when Hamlet arrives in England, he .... (kill).

7 Rosencrantz and Guildenstern .... (ask) to watch Hamlet carefully.

8 Laertes .... (trick) by Claudius into killing Hamlet.

Grammar: The definite article 'the'

Add 'the' to the sentence if necessary.

1 "All has been quiet tonight. ....*The*.... ghost has not appeared."

2 .... sudden decisions are sometimes better than plans.

3 .... King and Queen of Denmark are shocked by the play.

4 Gertrude drinks .... wine with the poison in it.

5 Ophelia returns .... gifts that Hamlet had given her.

6 Hamlet's father was killed by .... poison.

7 Hamlet thinks that .... women cannot be trusted.

8 Everyone thinks that Gertrude has fainted at .... sight of all the blood.

101

Word focus

Now complete the table with the missing words. The missing words are all in the story of Hamlet.

NOUN	VERB	ADJECTIVE
1 *tragedy*		tragic
2	flatter	flattering
starvation	3	starving
disobedience	disobey	4
bet	5	
6	warn	warning
7	behave	
8	speak	spoken

Complete the sentences with one of the words from the table.

1 When you are very hungry, you can say 'I'm ....'.

2 A story with a very sad ending, where many people die, is called a
....

3 People often feel nervous if they have to make a ....

4 When you .... money, sometimes you win more
money and sometimes you lose it all.

5 If you don't do what your parents ask you to do, then you
.... your parents.

6 If you tell someone how nice they look or how clever they are, then
you .... them.

7 Hamlet's .... (the way he acts) is quite strange.

8 Nobody was able to .... Hamlet about Claudius' plan
to kill him.

Making questions

Write questions for the answers.

> **Example:** *Who wrote 'Hamlet'?*
> Shakespeare wrote 'Hamlet'.

Q1	What
A1	The guards had seen the ghost of King Hamlet.
Q2	What
A2	The ghost told Hamlet that he had been murdered by his brother.
Q3	Why
A3	The play made Claudius angry because it showed a king being killed.
Q4	How
A4	Hamlet was angry with his mother.
Q5	Why
A5	Hamlet had to leave Denmark because he had killed Polonius.
Q6	How
A6	Ophelia drowned.
Q7	What
A7	Claudius told Laertes that Hamlet had killed his father.
Q8	Who
A8	Horatio told everyone the whole story at the end.

Macmillan Education
4 Crinan Street
London N1 9XW
A division of Macmillan Publishers Limited
Companies and representatives throughout the world

ISBN 978–0–230–71663–6

This version of *Hamlet* was retold by Margaret Tarner for Macmillan
Readers.
First published 2009
Text © Macmillan Publishers Limited 2009
Design and illustration © Macmillan Publishers Limited 2009

Illustrated by Fausto Bianchi
Cover photograph by Alamy/Alain Couillaud

Printed and bound in Thailand

2020   2019   2018   2017
16   15   14   13   12   11